Connecting With
God

A study series for growing disciples on foundational
connection points with God.

Christopher B. Adsit
Executive Director of Disciplemakers International
A ministry of Campus Crusade for Christ International

Other materials available from Disciplemakers International:

Personal Disciplemaking by Christopher B. Adsit, (Orlando, FL: Integrated Resources, 1988, 1996) This book presents a long term, disciple-sensitive, training objective oriented approach to one-on-one and small group disciplemaking. (ISBN: 1-57902-022-4)

Personal Disciplemaking Tool Kit contains supplemental material to be used with the book, *Personal Disciplemaking*. Included are the Self-Assessment Questionnaires, Key and Instructions, Disciple's Growth Profile Chart and Disciplemaking Growth Grid.

Personal Disciplemaking Mini Tool Kit contains just the Christian Fundamentals material from the full Tool Kit. This mini kit can be used as a "quick assessment" tool.

Personal Disciplemaking Video Training Series was produced in conjunction with Western Seminary in Portland, Oregon. This 24 session series provides training and materials to establish both lay people and "professional" Christians in the process of making disciples.

Disciplemaker's Encyclopedia **Resource Packets** contain information and resources which the disciplemaker can use when addressing specific issues in the life of the person they are discipling. Illustrations, Great Quotes, Bible Studies, Articles, and Additional Resources provide a wealth of information to choose from. Resource Packets completed to date include: *Assurance of Salvation* and *Praying With Others*.

PO Box 2212
Eugene OR 97402-0044
U.S.A.

Voice (541) 345-3458
Toll-free 1-888-342-2235 (within the U.S.A.)
Fax (541) 345-4249
www.ccci.org/disciplemakers
disciplemaker@compuserve.com

Disciplemakers International is a ministry of Campus Crusade for Christ International. Our purpose is to help mobilize Christians around the world to more efficiently and effectively pursue the fulfillment of the Great Commission of Jesus Christ (Matthew 28:19-20) by providing resources, motivation and training in need-oriented, in-depth, multiplying disciplemaking.

"And we proclaim Him, admonishing every man and teaching every man with all wisdom, that we may present every man complete in Christ. And for this purpose also I labor, striving according to His power, which mightily works within me."
—Colossians 1:28-29

Connecting With God
ISBN 0-9671227-3-2
© 2001 Christopher B. Adsit
All rights reserved.

First Printing July 2001; Second Printing September 2001

Unless otherwise noted, all Scripture references are taken from the Holy Bible, New International Version. Copyright © 1973, 1978, 1984 by International Bible Society. Scripture references marked (NAS) are taken from the New American Standard Bible, © 1960, 1962, 1963, 1968, 1971, 1972, 1973, 1975, 1977 by the Lockman Foundation, La Habra, CA. Used by permission. Scripture references marked (TLB) are taken from the Living Bible, © 1971 by Tyndale House Publishers, Wheaton, IL. Scripture references marked (NKJV) are taken from the Holy Bible, New King James Version, © 1979, 1980, 1982 by Thomas Nelson, Inc., Nashville, TN. Scripture references marked by (AMP) are taken from The Amplified Bible, © 1965 by Zondervan Publishing House, Grand Rapids, MI. Scripture references marked by (The Message) are taken from The Message, © 1993 by Eugene Peterson.

Table of Contents

Preface:

   Why This Bible Study Exists ii

Introduction:

   Spiritual Growth: Connecting Your Will To His Desire iv

Assessment:

   Personal Assessment Questionnaire: Connecting With Yourself vi

Bible Studies:

To be completed by the growing disciple — either alone (to be reviewed later with your mentor) or together with your mentor.

   Chapter 1:   The Assurance Connection: How Sure Can You Be? 1

   Chapter 2:   The Significance Connection: What Happened To YOU? 7

   Chapter 3:   The Power Connection: The Ministry Of The Holy Spirit 15

   Chapter 4:   The Victory Connection: Neglecting Your Old Nature 25

   Chapter 5:   The Growth Connection: Actions And Attitudes To Optimize Your Journey 33

   Chapter 6:   The Fellowship Connection: God Working On You Through Other Christians . 41

   Chapter 7:   The Bible Connection: God's Nourishment For Your Soul 49

   Chapter 8:   The Prayer Connection: Communing With The Wisest Being In History 59

   Chapter 9:   The Witnessing Connection: Spreading His Connections Around 69

   Chapter 10: The Warfare Connection: Dealing With Our Adversary 77

   Chapter 11: The Time Connection: God's Priorities Reflected In Your Calendar 87

   Chapter 12: The Vision Connection: What God Wants To Do With Your Life 97

   Bonus Chapter: The Devotional Connection: Your Secret Life With Jesus 107

Thought/Discussion Questions:

To enhance the content and stimulate the discussion of each study. If you are completing this study solo (with no mentor) these are "Thought Questions" for your consideration. If you are completing the study with a mentor, they are "Discussion Questions" for later use (either one-to-one or in a group context).

   Introduction: Continuing the Connection: How to Make The Most of This Section 115

   For Chapter 1: The Assurance Connection 116

   For Chapter 2: The Significance Connection 118

   For Chapter 3: The Power Connection 120

   For Chapter 4: The Victory Connection 122

   For Chapter 5: The Growth Connection 124

   For Chapter 6: The Fellowship Connection 126

   For Chapter 7: The Bible Connection 128

   For Chapter 8: The Prayer Connection 130

   For Chapter 9: The Witnessing Connection 132

   For Chapter 10: The Warfare Connection 134

   For Chapter 11: The Time Connection 136

   For Chapter 12: The Vision Connection 138

   For Bonus Chapter: The Devotional Connection 140

Appendices:

   1: Would You Like To Know God Personally? 143

   2: Principles For Memorizing Scripture 148

   3: Two Wells Illustration 149

   4: Spiritual Warfare Ammunition Bunker 150

   5: Reproducible Forms 153

   6: Disciplemakers International Order Form 159

Why This Bible Study Exists

I came to know Jesus Christ as my Savior in April of my freshman year at Colorado State University when a fellow student, Dick Kreider, shared the gospel with me. Immediately following my conversion and for the next two years, Dick "discipled" me – that is, he took a special interest in me, helping me to become someone who was eager to learn everything that Jesus Christ wanted to teach me. He began taking me to church each Sunday and showed me how to study the Bible. He prayed *with* me and *for* me faithfully, taught me how to have a daily "Quiet Time" with God, how to memorize scripture and how to share my faith. He got me involved with the Navigator movement on campus, answered my multitudinous questions about God and the Bible – or helped me find the answers. Though he was only two years older than I was, Dick was like a father to me. He was an awesome teacher, nurturer, example and friend.

When Dick graduated and went on to seminary, Wayne Feigal – another student at CSU – took over where Dick had left off and helped move me further down the road to spiritual maturity. When Wayne also headed for seminary after a year, Jay Wheeler, the Navigator Staff representative on campus took me on for my final year in Fort Collins and taught me many practical principles of leadership. Because of the diligent, encouraging, faithful mentoring of these three men, I was thoroughly grounded in my faith right off the bat, and equipped for a lifetime of growth and fruitfulness. To be sure, "God caused the growth," as it says in 1 Corinthians 3:6-7, but Dick, Wayne and Jay did some significant planting and watering during those years.

As it turned out, I had some talent in the area of track and field, and upon graduation felt led to join the Athletes in Action Track Team, part of the athletic ministry of Campus Crusade for Christ. During my first couple of years with AIA, I received even more terrific spiritual training from the largest and most prolific para-church ministry on the planet.

But I also realized something during those years: the mentoring I had received from Dick, Wayne and Jay was very rare and precious. Far from being the common occurrence that I thought it was, I found out that hardly anybody receives such attention after they become a Christian. This bugged me – a lot. I realized that most Christians have been trained in a very haphazard way, with no clear learning objectives, no curricula, no progress assessment and hardly anyone taking the time to see if they were actually learning anything. We'd *never* subject our children to such treatment in our schools, and yet this is standard treatment for the children of God.

When I became director of the Athletes in Action Track Team in 1978, it became my quest to come up with an objective yet flexible way to disciple the Track Team staff, and to train them how to disciple the athletes that God brought our way. Thus began a ten-year process of Bible study, research, interviewing and writing – which grew *way* beyond the scope of the Track Team.

In 1988, I published my first book entitled *Personal Disciplemaking.* The purpose of that book was to provide practical instruction and tools for anyone who was serious about becoming a need-oriented disciplemaker. In the book I provided twelve key Training Objectives for the disciplemaker to focus on as he or she works in partnership with the Holy Spirit to get a new Christian established in their walk with God. It also contained assessment tools that the disciplemaker could use to help determine the disciple's current spiritual status, where his or her strengths and weaknesses lay, and what issues needed to be addressed urgently.

In the years since that book was published, it became clear that one of the tools that would greatly enhance the system would be a Bible study series that exactly parallels the twelve Training Objectives. So, upon the urging of many respected associates, I've come up with this series. If you're already familiar with *Personal Disciplemaking,* what you read in each of its Training Objective chapters will provide a nice foundation for leading your disciple through the twelve chapters in this study.

Though the "mentor-facilitated" approach was my original intention for this series, it can also be used quite successfully in a group study situation, or by an individual who doesn't have a mentor but who is motivated to get out there and "dig his/her own wells." In any case, once you've completed the study and considered the "Thought/Discussion Questions" at the end of the book, you should then consider taking others through it. This is where the multiplication comes in! Don't let the chain end with you – keep it going! "And the things which you have heard from me in the presence of many witnesses, these entrust to faithful men, who will be able to teach others also." (**2 Timothy 2:2**).

Acknowledgments

As I put this study together, I was helped along the way by several people, and I want to thank and honor them here. The indispensable person in this venture was Karen Watkins, class-mate at Colorado State, fellow Navigator in those days, and presently my lone associate and peer (besides my wife Rahnella) here at Disciplemakers International. Her faithfulness, commitment and amazing expertise and diligence in editing, formatting, computering, researching, brainstorming, giving feedback, testing, communicating with testers, publishers, etc., and tweaking content is legendary and will be forever appreciated!

There were four who did the lion's share of reviewing, proof-reading, editing and clarifying many points I was lamely trying to make: Leslie Burton, Jan Kohler, Ruth Linoz and Dr. Linda Schrock. These women spent hours and hours poring over what I'd written, and making it turn out a *lot* better than it would have! Thank you!

A number of pastors and lay-leaders agreed to test the series – even as I was cranking out the individual studies – and to give me feedback. Their responses were always so encouraging, and gave me the umph and enthusiasm I needed to keep going. I haven't heard back from everyone as I write this, but from these folks I have: Bill Chadwick, Courtney Davey, Adrian Hartopp, Steve Lawson, Chuck Macri, Bob & June Marshall, Debbie Newland, Kent Ragsdale, Jim Rinella, Sandy Smith, and Jamie Stata. Thank you *all* for your participation and great feedback! For those who haven't gotten back to me yet, and whom I can't publicly thank right now – great will be your reward in heaven!

Thanks to Lloyd Olson, my former director, who gave me the idea for this series in the first place. Long time coming, eh? Thanks to Dan Meininger – the most faithful and potent co-discipler and prayer-backer a guy ever had. Focus, passion and intimacy with God! Thanks to Jay Wheeler, who continues to have strong input in my life even today, and got me on a schedule to get this thing actually *done!* Muchas gracias to Tim Cole, who provided us with the excellent Adobe software to construct this study. To the staff and congregation of Calvary Church of Santa Ana, who have faithfully and generously backed my ministry for almost a quarter of a century, my heart-felt gratitude.

Lastly, and most importantly, thanks to my wife Rahnella, whose constant love, encourage-ment, faith, prayers, and willingness to keep the home fires burning while I worked on this project have kept me encouraged, focused and motivated all along the way. You're the *best*, Poopsie!

Chris Adsit
Eugene, Oregon
June, 2001

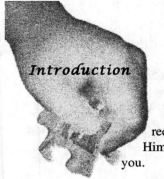

Spiritual Growth...
...Connecting Your Will To His Desire

Many people feel they "connected" with God once-and-for-all the moment they received Christ. And in terms of establishing an eternal, life-changing relationship with Him, they're right! But there are many, many more connections that God wants to make with you.

Prayer Seed:
The prayer in the little box at the beginning of each chapter can be a guide to you in what you can pray as you start working on the lesson.

"I came that they might have life and might have it abundantly."
—**John 10:10b**
[NAS]

You are an incredibly complex being. God wants to connect with your thought life, your priorities, your education, your recreation, your love life, your devotional life, your past, your future, your money, your time, your hopes and dreams. The list is as long as you are deep! His desire is to be "one" with you in every area of your life, so that the things He loves and pursues are the same things you want to love and pursue—with all your heart. He wants to maximize and optimize everything about you, and as your Creator, He knows exactly how to go about it!

From the day of your conception—and even before that—God has had two primary objectives regarding you: First, to save you from an eternity separated from Him, and second, to make you like His Son, Jesus Christ. Objective #1 can be accomplished in an instant. Objective #2 takes a lifetime. It's a process that begins at the moment of spiritual birth and will continue until either you've been made absolutely perfect—like Jesus was when He walked the earth in human form—or until you die and join Him in heaven.

So far, no one besides Jesus Christ has reached absolute perfection here on earth. But don't let that discourage you! The farther you progress down the road to spiritual maturity, the more you'll experience the "abundant" life that God has in mind for you (**John 10:10b**). As you grow spiritually, you will increasingly sense His closeness, His hand of blessing on your life, His guidance in your decisions. Your joy and sense of purpose will deepen as your usefulness to Him increases. Your desire and ability to do right and avoid wrong will be strengthened. Your love for Him and for others will be purified. Your priorities will line up with His. Your vision and discernment regarding the realities of the Kingdom of God will sharpen. Day by day, you'll look, act and react more and more like the Lord Jesus Christ, God's template for development for all of us.

Part of this transformation is God's sovereign responsibility, but part of it is ours. God has taken the initiative with us: "No one can come to Me unless the Father who sent Me draws him..." (**John 6:44**). But His initiative-taking activities didn't stop when we received Christ. He is continually knocking on the door of our hearts, asking:

- Will you let Me give you more?
- Will you let Me fix this?
- Will you let Me change that?
- Will you let Me add this?
- Will you let Me take that away?

How we respond to His requests will have a strong bearing on the pace, direction, depth and final outcome of our journey toward spiritual maturity. If we respond to Him positively, more and more connections to God will be established, and we will grow. If we respond negatively, we will stagnate. How this grieves His great heart! There is so much He desires to give us, do for us, and partner with us! But if we refuse to allow Him access to our lives—neglecting or rejecting those connections with Him—He won't force Himself on us. He'll wait patiently in the margins of our lives until we finally come around to His way of thinking, open our hearts to Him, and respond in love and obedience.

The main objective of this study series is to help you recognize and respond positively to the connections God wants to make with you. As you progress through these pages, please keep the following points in mind:

1. You'll get out of it what you put into it.

2. God is not interested in mere intellectual assent from you. Let the truths that you learn from Him—through the agency of this study—sink down from your brain into your heart and become convictions. And then let those convictions travel to your hands, feet and mouth in the form of application. He wants to change your life, not to simply stuff your head with information!

3. As you study the Bible in the context of this series, God is going to be asking you to make some important decisions. No one will force you in these decisions. They will be between you and God. But remember: to **not** make a decision when He asks you to **is** to make a decision.

4. We will spend all of our eternal lives getting to know God (**John 17:3**). This study is meant to aid in that process. Throughout your times in these pages, don't make "Finishing The Lesson" your goal. Make it "Getting To Know God A Little Better." As you approach each lesson, pray this simple prayer: **"What would You like to teach me today, Father?"**

5. Don't assume that when you are done with this study series, you're done growing. You'll be establishing key connections with God—or strengthening ones that already exist—but this is only the beginning. Become determined to be Jesus Christ's active, lifelong "learner."

Where Do I Start?

There is a saying that goes, "If you aim at nothing, you'll hit it every time." It's always more efficient if we can define a few targets before we start shooting!

What connections to God already exist in your life? Which ones are weak? Which ones are strong? Where do you need some major attention, and where do you just need a little tinkering? What crucial needs do you have right now? To help you answer these questions, complete the **Personal Assessment Questionnaire** that follows this Introduction. Most people find it instructive and motivational to do a little objective self-evaluation every now and then. You might be surprised at what you discover as you respond to the questions!

Study Options:

Individually. Complete each study in sequence, or take them out of sequence according to your own sense of need. Consider the questions in the Thought/Discussion chapters that correspond to each study. Write your answers out—the writing process helps to crystallize your thoughts.

Group. Each group member could complete the chapter studies on their own, and then go over the questions in the Thought/Discussion chapters together. Or, if your bunch doesn't have the time for "homework," complete the studies as a group.

Group With Assessment. After each group member has gone through the Personal Assessment Questionnaire on his/her own, come together and discuss your answers. Try to identify areas of common need and go through the studies linked to those areas first.

Just as you do not need to do every chapter nor do them in sequence (depending on assessed need), you may find that you will want to take more than one session to discuss a single chapter. Let these studies be your servant, not your master!

Personal Assessment Questionnaire...
...Connecting With Yourself

Directions: Answer each question by entering a number from 1 to 5 in the blanks on the left, where "1" means "This statement isn't true of me at all," and "5" means "This statement is exactly true about me." If you have no idea what the statement is talking about, put down a "1." The numbers you enter are *not* an indication of how good or bad you are, but of how much the indicated chapter will probably be of help to you. **Remember:** the main objective of this assessment is to help you highlight areas of need in your life to which you can give attention, *not* to make a statement regarding your "Christian performance" or your "level of spirituality."

Range 1 to 5:
1 = Not true about me at all
5 = Exactly true about me

Chapter 1: The Assurance Connection

1. _____ I am positive that, if I were to die today, I would immediately go to heaven.

2. _____ I have received Jesus Christ into my life; I've "opened the door" of my life to Him.

3. _____ I have a thorough understanding of what the Bible is talking about when it says I am a "new creation."

4. _____ I am positive that all my sins have been forgiven, and I now am considered righteous and acceptable in God's eyes.

5. _____ I am positive that my salvation is permanent, and that I will never again be separated from God.

6. _____ Even though some days I may not *feel* close to God, I never question my salvation or His presence in me.

Chapter 2: The Significance Connection

7. _____ I have a thorough understanding of the many significant changes that occurred in me after I asked Christ into my life.

8. _____ I am positive that before I met Christ and invited Him into my life, I was a sinner headed for hell.

9. _____ I understand what happened to the main thing that was keeping me separated from God: my sinfulness.

10. _____ I understand what the terms "redeemed" and "reconciled" mean and how I became redeemed and reconciled to God.

Chapter 3: The Power Connection

11. _____ I fully realize that a Christian must be filled (controlled and empowered) by the Holy Spirit in order to experience the abundant, victorious and satisfying life that God intended.

12. _____ I have a thorough understanding of how to be filled with the Holy Spirit.

13. _____ I walk in the fullness of the Holy Spirit most of the time.

14. _____ I have a thorough understanding of what to do to restore fellowship between God and myself when I have sinned.

Chapter 4: The Victory Connection

15. _____ I have a thorough understanding of the tension that exists between my new nature and my old nature and why I still struggle with temptation even though I am a "new creation."

16. _____ I am aware of practical, day-to-day things I can do to minimize the influence of my old nature and strengthen the influence of my new nature.

17. _____ I know what is meant by the term "the renewing of the mind" found in Romans 12:2, and I have a thorough understanding of how to go about it.

18. _____ I have taken significant steps to separate myself from the sinful practices I engaged in before I knew Jesus Christ as my Savior.

Chapter 5: The Growth Connection

19. _____ I have a thorough understanding of the activities I can undertake that will help me grow spiritually in a balanced, steady fashion.

20. _____ I realize that God plays a part in my spiritual growth and that I play a part. To the best of my abilities, I'm doing my part.

21. _____ I feel quite confident regarding my engagement in the four spiritual disciplines of the Christian life: Prayer, Bible Study, Fellowship and Witnessing.

22. _____ I know that adversity is a normal component of my life, allowed by God to help me grow stronger.

23. _____ When I experience trials, I never get mad at God but instead go to Him for help.

Range 1 to 5:
1 = Not true about me at all
5 = Exactly true about me

Chapter 6: The Fellowship Connection

24. _____ I have a thorough understanding of why it is important for me to be actively involved in fellowship with other Christians.

25. _____ I understand the differences between true Biblical fellowship and just "hanging around" other Christians socially.

26. _____ I attend church services, Bible studies or other fellowships [rarely or never = 1; once a month = 2; less than once a week = 3; once a week = 4; two or more times a week = 5].

27. _____ I understand the concept of "Christian accountability" and feel comfortable receiving and giving it.

Chapter 7: The Bible Connection

28. _____ I know very well what people mean when they call the Bible the "Word of God."

29. _____ I understand fully why it is so important to have a steady intake of the Bible.

30. _____ I know who wrote the Bible.

31. _____ I read, study and meditate on the Bible [rarely or never = 1; once a week = 2; 3x a week = 3; 5x a week = 4; at least once a day = 5].

32. _____ The percentage of the Bible that I have read is [little or none = 1; some of the New Testament (NT) and a little of the Old Testament (OT) = 2; all of the NT and a little of the OT = 3; all of the NT and about half of the OT = 4; 100% = 5].

Chapter 8: The Prayer Connection

33. _____ I know that prayer is simply talking to God, and I don't have any real difficulty doing it.

34. _____ I understand why some of my prayers are not answered.

35. _____ My prayer life is characterized by a good balance of Adoration (worship), Confession (of sins), Thanksgiving (for what God has done), and Supplication (sharing your requests with God).

36. _____ I have a period of personal, concentrated prayer [rarely or never = 1; once a week = 2; 3x a week = 3; 5x a week = 4; daily = 5].

37. _____ The "faith level" of my prayer life is [1 = very low; 5 = very high].

Chapter 9: The Witnessing Connection

38. _____ I have a thorough understanding of why every Christian ought to share the gospel with non-Christians whenever God provides the opportunity.

39. _____ I feel strongly motivated about telling others how they might come to a saving knowledge of Christ.

40. _____ Right now, I could do a great job of telling another person how to become a Christian.

41. _____ I could clearly present my testimony to a non-Christian of how I became a Christian.

42. _____ I understand what my role is in witnessing and what God's role is.

Range 1 to 5:
1 = Not true about me at all
5 = Exactly true about me

Chapter 10: The Warfare Connection

43. _____ I have a pretty thorough grasp of what the term "Spiritual Warfare" means.

44. _____ I understand Satan's origin and his eternal destination.

45. _____ I have a pretty thorough grasp of Satan's objectives and tactics.

46. _____ I am well trained and experienced in "resisting the devil."

47. _____ I realize that adversity in my life comes from several sources, not just from Satan.

Chapter 11: The Time Connection

48. _____ I am very good at setting godly priorities, crafting meaningful goals and managing my time with diligence and efficiency.

49. _____ I have a very clear idea about what I want to accomplish in my life, and I feel like I'm making progress.

50. _____ God really is the Lord of my daily time schedule. I feel He is definitely in control.

51. _____ I'm very good at planning ahead.

52. _____ I rarely feel stressed or anxious about my daily workload.

Chapter 12: The Vision Connection

53. _____ I feel a firm and settled conviction that God intends to use me in significant ways to advance His kingdom on earth.

54. _____ I feel a strong concern about what God is doing world-wide, not just within my narrow sphere of experiences.

55. _____ I understand the significance of the "Great Commission of Jesus Christ" found in Matthew 28:19-20.

56. _____ I can give an objective, Bible-based definition of the word "disciple."

57. _____ I have a good grasp of what's important to God and how these values relate to His plans for me.

Bonus Chapter: The Devotional Connection

58. _____ I have a "Quiet Time" with God just about every day.

59. _____ My main motivations in having a Quiet Time are to get to know God better and to deepen my relationship with Him.

60. _____ My Quiet Times contain a good balance of prayer and Bible study.

61. _____ I look forward with eagerness to my private times with Jesus.

62. _____ I feel comfortable with the length of my Quiet Times – not too long, and not too short.

Range 1 to 5:
1 = Not true about me at all
5 = Exactly true about me

Making The Assessment

Each question reflects material that will be addressed in its corresponding chapter. Question Clusters for each chapter that seem to have many 1's and 2's indicate areas of need, while Clusters with lots of 4's and 5's indicate areas of strength. You can elect to take the chapters in this study in their arranged sequence, or you could go directly to chapters that seem to address crucial assessed needs in your life. Question Clusters that have mainly 3's and 4's indicate areas that are partially established in your life but could use some strengthening. If you have Question Clusters for some chapters with a majority of 5's, don't get the idea that you couldn't use any additional input in those areas. You might want to visit those chapters for refreshment and possibly some additional perspectives.

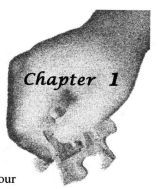

The Assurance Connection...
...How Sure Can You Be?

Chapter 1

Why Make This Connection?

If you have doubts about whether or not you are saved—or if you base the validity of your salvation on the wrong things—it will be difficult to remain confident and faithful in your Christian walk when the storms of life come your way. In addition, you have an enemy named Satan who will try to convince you that your decision to receive Christ was hollow, ineffective, even imaginary. Some Christians live their whole lives in fear they'll lose their salvation if they commit a certain vague sin. Some fear they were never saved in the first place, due to some sin they think is beyond God's willingness to forgive. As you'll learn in this study, the Bible says we Christians can *know*—with no doubts—that we are eternally saved and headed for heaven, despite what our feelings, circumstances or the devil may try to tell us.

What Were You Expecting?

When it comes to visualizing the supernatural, many people take their cues from Hollywood. In that world of make-believe, people who encounter dimensions other than the one we normally live in always get flashes of light, exciting "Surroundsound" music, The Force imparting miraculous powers, inter-dimensional visions, and angels ricocheting off the walls. From then on, all they have to do is tap their heels together three times, and all their problems are solved.

But in the *real* world, when we enter into a *real* relationship with the *real* God of the universe, it's usually not so dramatic. This is confusing to some people. To be sure, a few people *do* get the ricocheting-angels treatment. Some have very profound emotional experiences or are overwhelmed with a sense of peace or forgiveness. But usually, it doesn't happen that way.

Think back to when you received Jesus Christ into your heart. Can you remember some of the expectations you had? Write them down here. Were your expectations fulfilled?

Prayer Seed: "Father, help me sense Your closeness and experience the witness of Your Spirit to my spirit. Give me that quiet confidence in my heart that I belong to You. Amen."

Think About It: Do you think we should rely on Hollywood, or our culture, or our own imaginations when looking for realistic expectations about God and how He interacts with people? Probably not. A much more reliable authority would be the source for *all* of our information about God, His Son Jesus Christ, salvation, heaven and hell, and much more: **The Bible.**

"What Can I Be Sure About?"

What does the Bible say you can be sure about when you asked Jesus Christ to be your Savior? Let's look at five key points.

> "Here I am! I stand at the door and knock. If anyone hears My voice and opens the door, I will come in and eat with him, and he with Me."
> —Revelation 3:20

1 You can be sure Christ has come into your life.

What do you think "the door" in the verse to the left represents?

What does Jesus say He'll do if a person opens that door?

How do you think one "opens the door" to Jesus?

Have you done that? If so, when?

> "But as many as received Him, to them He gave the right to become children of God, even to those who believe in His name."
> —John 1:12 [NAS]

Read John 1:12. According to this verse, what two things does a person need to do in order to be called a child of God?

1. _____

2. _____

Have you done those two things? If so, when?

> If you're not sure you have actually taken that step of inviting Christ into your life as your Savior, go to Appendix #1 for some insight on how to go about it.

2 You can be sure you were "reborn" as a "new creation."

Becoming a Christian isn't like joining a club or taking out an insurance policy. And it's not simply adopting a new philosophy. When you received Jesus Christ into your life, you were *literally* changed into a new being!

> "Therefore, if anyone is in Christ, he is a new creation; the old has gone, the new has come!"
> —2 Corinthians 5:17

Read 2 Corinthians 5:17. Since you have invited Christ into your life, you are said to be "in Christ." He's in you, and you're in Him! What does this verse say is true of those who are "in Christ"?

When the Bible says "the old has gone," what do you think it's talking about?

What would you say is some of the "new" that has come into your life?

Find and read **John 3:1-10** in your Bible. Before Nicodemus met Jesus, was he a very religious person? (see especially verses 1 & 10)

And yet, Jesus told Nicodemus he still had a great need. What was it? (verses 3 & 5)

> **Other Bible writers on the topic of being born spiritually:**
>
> **Peter:** "For you have been born again, not of perishable seed, but of imperishable, through the living and enduring word of God."   —**1 Peter 1:23**
>
> **John:** "For everyone born of God overcomes the world. This is the victory that has overcome the world, even our faith."   —**1 John 5:4**

3 *You can be sure all your sins—past, present and future—have been forgiven.*

> "But your iniquities have separated you from your God; your sins have hidden His face from you, so that He will not hear."   —**Isaiah 59:2**
>
> "The soul who sins is the one who will die."   —**Ezekiel 18:20a**
>
> "For the wages of sin is death."   —**Romans 6:23a**

According to the three verses above, what has kept us apart from God and would eventually lead us to eternal death?

According to the three verses below, what has become of your sins now that you have confessed them to God and asked Christ to be your Savior?

Psalm 32:5 _____

Psalm 103:12 _____

Isaiah 43:25 _____

> **The Point:** If our sins were keeping us separate from God, what can we say about our connection with God now that our sins are no longer an issue? It's re-established and permanent!

"Does this mean I won't sin any more?"

If you're human, you will still sin from time to time. But as you grow more mature in the Lord, those episodes will become fewer and farther apart.

"What should I do when I sin?"

Sin will always strain and hamper your relationship with God—that's why He says it's bad. But when we agree with Him regarding its "badness"—which is what confession is—God will forgive our sins, blot them out, cast them away from us and forget them. This clears the way for a renewed, unhindered connection with God.

> **Think About It:** In **John 3:5-6**, Jesus talked about being "born of water and of the Spirit." Being "born of water" refers to physical birth—everyone who has ever lived has been "born of water." But Jesus says that this doesn't qualify you to enter the kingdom of God. Since God's kingdom exists on a *spiritual* plane, we must also be born *spiritually*—a "second birth." When you asked Jesus Christ into your life, you were born into the spiritual realm. Prior to that, you were dead spiritually, only a two-dimensional being: physical and mental. But when Christ's Spirit entered your life, you gained a third dimension: spiritual! At long last, you and God are "on the same wavelength"!

> **Note:** *Iniquities, transgressions* and *sins* all refer to the same thing: breaking God's laws. The penalty for this: separation from Him.

> "If we confess our sins, He is faithful and just and will forgive us our sins and purify us from all unrighteousness."
> —**1 John 1:9**

4 You can be sure a new relationship has been established between you and God.

Before you received Christ into your life, you were dead spiritually, separated from God, guilty of sin and even called an "enemy of God" (**Romans 5:10**).

Look up the following verses in your Bible and write down how they describe your relationship with Him *now*. You may note several characteristics in some passages. In each case, complete this sentence:

"I once was lost, but now I'm..."

John 15:15 _____

Romans 8:14-17 _____

1 Corinthians 6:17 _____

Ephesians 2:19 _____

Amazing grace!
How sweet the sound,
That saved a wretch like me!
I once was lost, but now am found,
Was blind, but now I see!
–John Newton, 1779, from the hymn, "Amazing Grace"

5 You can be sure you will never again be separated from God.

"How long can I count on eternal life lasting?"

"Oh, sure," you might be saying. "Things are going pretty good right now. I feel really connected to God, and I want to please Him in every way possible. But what happens if, say, a year from now, I really blow it? I mean really, really, *really* blow it? Will God re-evaluate my status? Will He take back the life He gave me? Will He give up on me? I was separated from God before— could it happen again?"

The Apostle Paul's answer to that question is in **Romans 8:38-39**, printed on the left.

How many times does the word "except" appear in this passage? (Don't spend too much time looking for it — it's not there!) What does this tell you?

"For I am convinced that neither death nor life, neither angels nor demons, neither the present nor the future, nor any powers, neither height nor depth, nor anything else in all creation, will be able to separate us from the love of God that is in Christ Jesus our Lord."
—**Romans 8:38-39**

Look up the following verses in your Bible. Draw a line to match each reference on the left with the fact about your eternal security on the right.

John 6:37   • Nothing and no one can ever pull you out.

John 10:27-29   • God will never desert or forsake you.

Hebrews 13:5   • Jesus will never throw you out.

In other words, once you're in the family of God, you're in for good!

According to the passage to the right (**1 Peter 1:4-5**), who has reserved the gift of eternal life for you?

Does this give you confidence?

In what condition will it be kept for you?

Who will make sure you get there safely to receive it?

How many times do words or phrases such as "maybe", "possibly", "barring unforeseen circumstances" or "if all goes well" appear in this passage?

What does this tell you?

> "And God has reserved for His children the priceless gift of eternal life; it is kept in heaven for you, pure and undefiled, beyond the reach of change and decay. And God, in His mighty power, will make sure that you get there safely to receive it, because you are trusting Him. It will be yours in that coming last day for all to see."
> —1 Peter 1:4-5 [TLB]

"What if I don't 'feel' saved?"

Everyone is "wired" differently. Some people are quite emotional, others very calm and objective. Some seem intuitively aware of every tiny occurrence around them, while others tend to notice only nuclear explosions in their immediate neighborhood. How you respond to receiving Christ into your life will be greatly affected by how God has made you. But regardless of your "wiring," your feelings will come and go. It's important to base your convictions regarding what's real and what isn't on something more solid than feelings.

Look up **2 Corinthians 5:7** in your Bible. What does it say we "walk by" (or in some Bible translations, "live by")—that is, what are we supposed to depend on to regulate our lives, to determine right and wrong, to validate whether a certain course of action is the best one, etc.? Choose one of the following:

❑ Feelings   ❑ Suggestions of others   ❑ If it seems right
❑ Faith   ❑ Trial & error   ❑ Logic

But what do we base our faith on? In what do we place it?

This train diagram[1] illustrates the relationship between **fact, faith** and **feeling**. The engine, Fact, represents what we know to be true on the basis of the Word of God. The coal car, Faith, represents our

beliefs and our confidence in certain truths, which produce attitudes and actions in us. When we say we have faith in something, we are saying we believe it to be absolutely true, and we are willing to take action based on that belief.

The caboose, Feeling, represents our subjective, emotional sensitivities and impressions. The train will run with or without the caboose, but it goes nowhere without the engine. Also, the train moves only if you shovel coal from the coal car into the engine. The caboose has no ability to power a train. In the same way, our Christian lives will move only if we place our *faith* in the *facts* of God's Word. Looking to our feelings to validate our eternal status will always get us into trouble. But if we put our faith in the facts found in God's Word, our feelings will eventually tag along!

> **"Can God take back this salvation which Christ has purchased? Absolutely not! Since the debt was paid, for God to demand it again from us would be unrighteous. The same righteousness which formerly called for our condemnation now calls for our justification. What powerful security this gives to our salvation! Even a worldly judge would not demand the same fine to be paid twice."[2]**
> **–Watchman Nee**

Here's a summary of the five things you can be sure about now that you have asked Jesus Christ to be your Savior:

1. You can be sure Christ has come into your life.

2. You can be sure you were "reborn" as a "new creation."

3. You can be sure all your sins—past, present and future—have been forgiven.

4. You can be sure a new relationship has been established between you and God.

5. You can be sure you will never again be separated from God.

Personal Application:

How sure are you now?

On a scale of one to ten, how sure are you that if you were to die tonight, you would immediately go to heaven to spend eternity with God?

Not at all sure	1 2 3 4 5 6 7 8 9 10	*Absolutely sure*

If you circled anything less than "10," what is causing you to have doubts about this issue? What is keeping you from being "absolutely sure"?

Scripture Memory Verse:

The Assurance Connection—
"And this is the testimony: God has given us eternal life, and this life is in His Son. He who has the Son has life: he who does not have the Son of God does not have life."
—1 John 5:11-12

About 1 John 5:11-12: At my wedding my friend handed me an envelope. "This is for you and your wife," he said. Of course, I was quite offended. Why would my friend be so cheap as to give us an envelope as a wedding gift? I had plenty of envelopes at home in my desk. The nerve! But later, I looked *inside* the envelope and found a $100 bill! The very moment I received the envelope, I received the $100 bill. He who had the envelope, had the money. In the same way, when you received Jesus into your life, you also received eternal life, because eternal life is *in Jesus!*

Note: Why "Personal Application"? Don't study the Bible without intending to apply what you learn to your life. Do something about it!

Note: For some helpful principles on memorizing Scripture, see Appendix #2.

Wrap Up: Jesus asks you, "Will you trust Me with your eternity?"

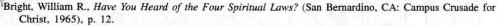

[1]Bright, William R., *Have You Heard of the Four Spiritual Laws?* (San Bernardino, CA: Campus Crusade for Christ, 1965), p. 12.
[2]Nee, Watchman, *The Assurance, Security and Joy of Salvation* (Living Stream Ministry), p. 5.

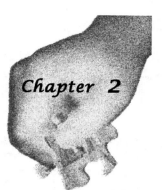

The Significance Connection...
...What Happened To YOU?

Chapter 2

Why Make This Connection?

Pierre Chanel had been trying to sell the dusty old painting from his flea market stall in Laraque, France, for three months. The canvas was only twelve inches by twenty-two inches and depicted the Virgin Mary holding two infants on her lap—presumably Jesus and John the Baptist. Finally, in May of 1999, school teacher Jacques Proust happened by and bought it for about seventy dollars. Chanel was glad to get rid of it and quite satisfied with his profit.

Proust wrapped his purchase in a blanket in the back of his van and decided to have it appraised by a local art dealer. The dealer was impressed and advised Proust to take it to Paris to have a more expert appraisal done. The painting was passed from one appraiser to another, until finally Renaissance expert Giovanni Fortini issued his verdict: the portrait was a lost Leonardo da Vinci, worth at least $50 million.

If Chanel had realized the incredible value of that little painting, do you think he would have committed what is probably the most expensive mistake in art history? Do you think he'd be selling art from a flea market stall anymore?

And what of Jacques Proust—how do you think his life has changed since he learned of the unimaginable treasure his seventy dollars had bought?

You also have made an incredible "purchase"—though it wasn't a purchase at all, but a free gift, which you accepted. If you can grasp the scope and significance of what you gained when you received Jesus Christ as your Savior, it would change your life as profoundly as Jacques Proust's was changed, even more so! That's the aim of this study—to highlight for you *what happened* when you became a Christian. What changed? What did you gain? What did you lose? How are you different?

We want you to be well informed of the assets you now own so that you can use them to the fullest! Don't sell yourself short and find yourself at the end of your life repeating stallholder Pierre Chanel's words: "I do feel slightly sick about it now . . ."

> **Prayer Seed:**
> "Father, I praise You for the wondrous things You've done in my life! But I think I understand only a tiny part of all You've done. Please enlighten me! Help me to know who I am now that You have come into my life and have made me a being that is equipped to function eternally! Amen."

First, the BAD Good News . . .
Your Condition Before Receiving Christ.

For many people, it's motivational to know what they were saved *from* when they entered the kingdom of God. Each of the four following passages describe your rather **negative** condition prior to receiving Christ...

According to **Romans 3:23**, I was a _____ .

> "For all have sinned, and fall short of the glory of God."
> —**Romans 3:23**

What do you think it means to "fall short of the glory of God?"

"But your iniquities have separated you from your God; your sins have hidden His face from you, so that He will not hear."
—**Isaiah 59:2**

According to **Isaiah 59:2**, I was _____ from God.

My prayers were _____

"Then I saw a great white throne and Him who was seated on it. Earth and sky fled from His presence, and there was no place for them. And I saw the dead, great and small, standing before the throne, and books were opened. Another book was opened, which is the book of life. The [spiritually] dead were judged according to what they had done as recorded in the books . . . Then death and Hades were thrown into the lake of fire. The lake of fire is the second death. If anyone's name was not found written in the book of life, he was thrown into the lake of fire."
—**Revelation 20:11-15**

Revelation 20:11-15 describes the final judgment and condemnation of those who did not trust Christ to be their Savior. Notice that they were tried on the basis of "what they had done." None of us could endure that judgment because we have *all* done wrong. But it says that some people's names were written in the "book of life." When you received Christ, *your* name was written there, and His perfect righteousness was transferred to your "account." The ledger of your sins is now irrelevant because God the Judge looks at Christ's perfect record instead of the *actual* record you amassed while on earth.

But before this "transaction of God's grace" occurred, what would have happened to you if you had died before being saved and had stood before God's "Great White Throne"?

"We are all infected and impure with sin. When we put on our prized robes of righteousness we find they are but filthy rags. Like autumn leaves we fade, wither and fall. And our sins, like the wind, sweep us away."
—**Isaiah 64:6** [TLB]

According to **Isaiah 64:6**, when I tried in my own strength to be "righteous" and acceptable before God, _____

_____

Nothing personal . . . No one's trying to single you out as some over-the-top dirty rotten sinner who isn't worth the mud it took to create you. You just need to know that your life before receiving Christ was not acceptable to God. Relative to other people, you might have been a very good person. But relative to God—whose standard for entrance into heaven is moral perfection—you wouldn't have made the cut. No offense, we ALL were in that boat at one time.

Next, the GOOD Good News . . .
Your Condition After Receiving Christ.

Following are twelve scripture passages that explain some important *positive* facts about what is true about the "new you" . . .

+1

"But when this priest [Jesus Christ] had offered for all time one sacrifice for sins, He sat down at the right hand of God. Since that time He waits for His enemies to be made His footstool, because by one sacrifice He has made perfect forever those who are being made holy."
—**Hebrews 10:12-14**

What sacrifice does **Hebrews 10:12-14** refer to?

What did this sacrifice make you?

Extra Insight: For more information on the reason for sacrifices in the Bible, see "The Structure of the Bible" in chapter 7, pages 51-52.

According to **Hebrews 10:17**, what does God think about your past sins now?

"Their sins and lawless acts I will remember no more."
—**Hebrews 10:17**

Extra Insight: Your problem as a non-Christian was that your sins had separated you from God and were pulling you to hell. God had told us all what was right and wrong, and He also told us of the consequences of our disobedience. Yet every one of us has refused to obey Him. A holy, righteous God can't just say, "Oh well, boys will be boys!" and let it slide. Something needed to be done about our sins. When they were paid for and removed from our record through the sacrifice of Jesus Christ, God no longer had any reason to keep His distance from us. So when He looks at you now, all He can see is the sinless righteousness of Jesus Christ. You have been *justified* before God, and now He sees you *"just-as-if-I'd"* never sinned. Worried about your sinful past? In God's eyes, you don't have one!

According to **Romans 8:11**, where does God's Holy Spirit now live?

"And if the Spirit of Him who raised Jesus from the dead is living in you, He who raised Christ from the dead will also give life to your mortal bodies through His Spirit, who lives in you."
—**Romans 8:11**

Note: Just because you have this new connection with the Holy Spirit, don't get the idea that you will no longer have any problems in life. However, it should encourage you that the Supreme Problem-Solver of the Universe is now as close to you as your heart and lungs!

More on this subject in Chapter 3, *The Power Connection.*

What did Jesus say a man had to do before he could see the kingdom of God? (verse 3)

Read John 3:1-10 in your Bible.

When Jesus referred to being "born of water" (verse 5) and "flesh gives birth to flesh" (verse 6), what kind of a birth was He talking about?

By The Way: Nicodemus eventually was born-again and became a follower of Christ. See **John 7:50-51** and **John 19:38-40**.

Has every human being experienced this kind of birth?

So being "born of the Spirit" (verses 5 and 8) must refer to what kind of birth?

Nicodemus was very "religious," and yet, had he experienced this second kind of birth?

Having received Christ, you can say for certain, "I have been born _____ !"

"And this is the testimony: God has given us eternal life, and this life is in His Son. He who has the Son has life; he who does not have the Son of God does not have life. I write these things to you who believe in the name of the Son of God so that you may know that you have eternal life."   —1 John 5:11-13

Where does the verse to the left say "eternal life" is located?

In relation to you, where is Jesus Christ now located?

"If our salvation is not secure, how could Jesus say about those to whom He gives eternal life, 'and they shall never perish' (John 10:28)? If even one man or woman receives eternal life and then forfeits it through sin or apostasy, will they not perish? And by doing so, do they not make Jesus' words a lie?"[1]
–Charles Stanley

Since you have received the Son of God into your life, what does this verse say you *also* now have?

What might cause your "eternal life" to come to an end?

Greek Lesson: When Jesus said He would give us "eternal" life, the Greek word He used was *aionios,* which means "indeterminate as to duration, eternal, everlasting, forever."[2] So, how long will your eternal life in Christ last? Could it ever end, be lost or go away? No, because then it never could have been called *aionios*. At best it would be "temporary eternal life," which is a fundamental contradiction of terms. Bottom line: the "eternal life" that Christ gives is eternal!

"Therefore, if anyone is in Christ, he is a new creation; the old has gone, the new has come!"
—2 Corinthians 5:17

Do you think you look any different physically since you received Christ into your life?

Spiritually, in ways that don't necessarily register with our five senses, you have been made *profoundly* different! So much so that the Bible calls you a "new creation"! For some people, their physical appearance *has* changed since becoming a Christian. This is an external manifestation of the changes that occurred internally. List a few physical, external changes that might be observable in someone who has been made a new creation spiritually.

What are some of the "old" things that are now gone from your life?

What are some of the "new" things that have come?

What do you think the term "reconciled" means?

"All this is from God, who reconciled us to Himself through Christ and gave us the ministry of reconciliation."
—2 Corinthians 5:18

We hear the term "reconciled" in divorce courts a lot, but in a little different form: "irreconcilable differences." Usually this means that one or both of the marriage partners decide they can't get along with the other person, they don't want to fix the relationship, and they want the other person to go away. In a way, this was how it was between you and God, except that while we may not have wanted Him, He *did* want us. The Father has been working a long time to draw you to Himself. Through Christ's death on the cross and the work of the Holy Spirit, He finally accomplished it. You're together again, and the divorce is off—permanently!

Read **Romans 5:1**. What is the opposite of "peace"?

"Therefore, since we have been justified through faith, we have peace with God through our Lord Jesus Christ."
—Romans 5:1

If we now have "peace with God" since we put our faith in Christ, what phrase would describe our relations with Him prior to becoming Christians?

"People may not realize that they're at war with God. But if they don't know Jesus Christ as Savior, and if they haven't surrendered to Him as Lord, God considers them to be at war with Him."
–Billy Graham

How did we come to be at war with God? The Bible says that thousands of years ago, before God created man, He created an enormous population of angels. The Number One angel, Lucifer, who was the most beautiful and intelligent of them all, decided he wanted to take over God's position as God. He convinced one-third of the angels to join him in his coup attempt, and a war followed that would make World War III look like a game of checkers. The forces of God won, and Lucifer (now called Satan) and his followers (now called demons) were thrown out of God's kingdom. But Satan has never changed his mind. He still wants to take God's place in people's lives – he wants to be obeyed and worshipped. When the first humans were created, he even convinced them to join his rebellion through disobedience to God. As a result, every one of their offspring has a natural tendency to rebel against God's authority.

At some time or another, each of us decided to join Satan's rebellion. It wasn't obvious to us at the time, but frankly we just didn't want God telling us what to do. Because of this stubborn self-will of ours, we became Satan's allies and God's enemies. But God loves His enemies. His battle strategy was to destroy His enemies by making them His friends and draw them with love to His side of the war. Those who agreed to His terms are now at *peace* with Him—His friends and allies.

If there's a war going on, and we are no longer God's enemies but His allies and soldiers, whom do we fight now, and how? (This is covered further in Chapter 10.)

For Further Insight on Satan's rebellion:
Isaiah 14:12-17
Ezekiel 28:11-19
Revelation 12:3-6
For Further Insight on who our enemy is:
Ephesians 6:10-12
See also Chapter 10, *The Warfare Connection.*

The word "redeem" in the verse to the right means "to buy out, especially of purchasing a slave with a view to his freedom."[3] In a very real sense, we had "sold" ourselves to Satan and were his slaves. In what ways were you personally a "slave" to Satan (areas where he influenced you to say "No" to God and "Yes" to him)?

"But when the time had fully come, God sent His Son, born of a woman, born under law, to redeem those under law, that we might receive the full rights of sons."
—Galatians 4:4-5

What did Jesus use to purchase us from this slave-market?

We are no longer slaves of Satan; now we are sons and daughters of God, with all the attending rights and privileges. What do you think some of these "rights" are that you now have?

> "For He has rescued us from the dominion of darkness and brought us into the kingdom of the Son He loves."
> —Colossians 1:13

Colossians 1:13 says that we were rescued from Satan's kingdom. Were we then cast adrift as refugees, left to fend for ourselves, or did we experience a different fate? If so, what?

"Faith is to believe —on the Word of God—what we cannot see, and its reward is to see and enjoy what we believed."

–St. Augustine

Think About It: As a new citizen of the kingdom of God, do your surroundings now look very different from before you knew Christ? Probably not. But a major component of the Christian life is believing in things you can't see. It's called *faith*. While we may not see any *physical* differences in our surroundings, in the unseen spiritual dimension we have truly been snatched out of the kingdom of darkness and placed into the kingdom of light. Satan is no longer our king, and we owe him no loyalty. We now swear our devotion to Jesus Christ. The more time we log in this new kingdom, the more clearly we'll be able to "see" it—in our attitudes, actions, allegiances, priorities and the circumstances that surround us daily.

+11

Read Romans 8:15-17 in your Bible.

According to this passage, which sentence *most accurately* portrays God's attitude toward you now that you've been redeemed?

❑ Now you can be on My team.
❑ Now you can come and live in My kingdom.
❑ Now I'll tolerate you, and allow you to hang around Me.
❑ Now you're My *child!*

Extra Insight:
Abba is an Aramaic word (a commonly spoken language in Jesus' day) that would be equivalent to our "Daddy!" It communicates a deep relationship, affection and familiarity.

What do you think is the greatest thing about having been "adopted" into God's family?

Notice what is written in verse 17, " … if indeed we share in His sufferings in order that we may also share in His glory." What message does this give to Christians who expect life to be all "moonlight and roses" from now on because of their new connection with God?

Though there is a battle going on, and though you cannot expect to have a hassle-free life as a Christian, what does this verse say you CAN expect?

"The angel of the Lord encamps around those who fear Him, and He delivers them."
—**Psalm 34:7** +12

As a child, you probably heard about "Guardian Angels." Well, it's more than a childish fantasy —it's reality! God has commissioned one or more angels to surround you for protection. Anything that gets to you must get through this potent perimeter first! And the Bible describes angels as very powerful beings. You can *count* on God to use these angels to protect you, as long as you fulfill *what prerequisite* mentioned in this verse?

For Further Insight: See **Proverbs 24:16**. The righteous man may fall, but then what happens?

What do you think it means to "fear" God?

> ➤   *Answer the above question before you proceed!*   ◄

For most of us, "fear" is being afraid of something evil that could cause us anxiety or pain. But the word has a different connotation when used in the Bible describing a believer's feelings toward his Redeemer. It means to have an attitude of obedience-producing reverence or awe toward God.[4] Since we are His children now, there's no need to be afraid that God intends evil or harm toward us. Because we recognize His awesome power and His amazing kindness to us, we hold Him in reverential respect. As we do this, we can have confidence that He will protect us. Now, would you change what you wrote about "fearing God" above?

Here's a summary of the four negative facts that are no longer true about you:

-1. You were a condemned sinner – **Romans 3:23**

-2. You were separated from God – **Isaiah 59:2**

-3. You were headed for hell – **Revelation 20:11-15**

-4. You were unable to please God – **Isaiah 64:6**

Here's a summary of the twelve positive facts that are now true about you:

+1. God has declared you perfect in His eyes – **Hebrews 10:12-14**

+2. Your sins have been forgiven and forgotten – **Hebrews 10:17**

+3. The Holy Spirit now lives within you – **Romans 8:11**

+4. You have been born again spiritually – **John 3:1-8**

+5. You have been given eternal life – **1 John 5:11-13**

+6. You have been made into a new creation – **2 Corinthians 5:17**

+7. You have been reconciled to God – **2 Corinthians 5:18**

+8. You are no longer at war with God – **Romans 5:1**

+9. You have been redeemed from slavery to Satan – **Galatians 4:4-5**

+10. You are now a citizen of God's Kingdom – **Colossians 1:13**

+11. You are now an adopted child of God – **Romans 8:15-17**

+12. You are now surrounded by a wall of supernatural protection – **Psalm 34:7**

Personal Application:

Once a day for the next three weeks (that's 21 days!) read over the two lists on the previous page and declare each fact out loud. But personalize it. For each of the four negative facts, change each "You were" to "I was." For each of the twelve positive facts, change each "you" and "your" to "me," "I" or "my." Don't turn it into a mindless chant or formalized ritual. Think about each statement as you say it, and let its truth sink into your soul. There is something powerful about making verbal declarations such as this. Not only will they increase your confidence about the changes that have occurred in you, but they will be a daily affirmation to both God and Satan regarding what you now know is true about you!

Checking in: How is Scripture Memory going for you? Review the principles in Appendix #2 for encouragement.

Scripture Memory Verse:

> **The Significance Connection—**
> "Therefore, if anyone is in Christ, he is a new creation; the old has gone, the new has come!"
> **—2 Corinthians 5:17**

Wrap Up:
Jesus asks you, "Will you realize who I made you to be?"

[1] Stanley, Charles, *Eternal Security: Can You Be Sure?* (Nashville, TN: Thomas Nelson, 1990), p. 18.

[2] Moulton, Harold K., *The Analytical Greek Lexicon Revised* (Grand Rapids, MI: Zondervan Publishing House, 1978), p. 11.

[3] Vine, W.E. *An Expository Dictionary of New Testament Words* (Old Tappan, NJ: F. H. Revell, 1940,1966), Vol. 3, p. 262.

[4] Harris, R. Laird, Archer, Gleason L., Waltke, Bruce K., *Theological Wordbook of the Old Testament* (Chicago, IL: Moody Press, 1980, 1981), Vol. I, pp. 399-400.

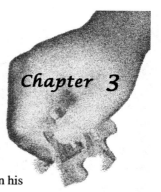

The Power Connection...
...The Ministry of the Holy Spirit

Chapter 3

Why Make This Connection?

A friend of mine recently invited me over for dinner. He had a smug, self-satisfied grin on his face throughout the meal. I knew something was up. When we finished dessert, it finally became clear why he as acting so superior.

"You know, I am now one of the most accomplished computer experts in this city," he said with casual pride.

"Are you now?" I replied. "How did this happen?"

He got up from the table and motioned me to his home office. "Follow me. I'll show you."

Occupying half of his office was the latest and greatest home computing system money could buy. "I set this baby up just last week. It's got a five terabyte hard drive, 1.5 gigabytes of turbo RAM, Pentium$_{TM}$ 12 processor running at two gigahertz, 95x DVD-CD ROM drive and a JumboTron video monitor!"

I couldn't help but be impressed. With such equipment, my friend could indeed accomplish some powerful computing. "Amazing!" I enthused. "This looks like one monstrous machine! What can it do?"

"Do? Why, it can do just about anything: word processing, graphics, video, spreadsheets, nuclear physics, heart surgery, crisis counseling, macramé, you name it! And fast as blazes, too!"

"Fantastic! Show me what you've done since you set it up."

My friend was silent for a moment. Finally he spoke, "That's the strange thing about this computer. It just sits there. I haven't actually done *anything* with it since I set it up. But who am I to question the user's manual—and all the other users who have spoken so highly of it?"

"Tell you what," I offered. "Let's turn it on and take a look at it." I located the on/off button and pushed it. Nothing happened. I pushed it three times. Still nothing. "Are you sure you plugged this thing in?" I asked.

"Plugged it in? What do you mean?"

_____

It doesn't matter how powerful a computer is—if it's not plugged in, it's nothing more than a very expensive dust catcher. In much the same way, a Christian who isn't "plugged in" to the plans and power of the Holy Spirit will not experience the fulfilling and useful life for which Jesus Christ has designed him.

This connection—the "Power Connection" between you and the Holy Spirit—will be the most important and helpful connection you'll make in your new life with God.

Wait A Minute . . .

You may be thinking to yourself, "I'm confused. I thought the Holy Spirit entered my life when I accepted Jesus Christ to be my Lord and Savior. Doesn't that mean I'm already 'plugged in'? How could I be a Christian and *not* be plugged in to the Holy Spirit?"

There is a difference between being "indwelt" by the Holy Spirit and being "filled" by the Holy Spirit. Not understanding this distinction—and how to stay in the "filled" condition—accounts for many Christians living lives of defeat and disappointment.

Read on, to learn the differences between the two...

Prayer Seed:
"Father, without Your help, I can't live the kind of life that both You and I desire. I need Your insight, Your direction, Your power! Please show me how to let You live Your life through me. Amen."

"No truth is more important to the believer than an understanding of the person and ministry of the Holy Spirit and how to be filled and controlled by Him as a way of life by faith."

–Bill Bright

Indwelt by the Holy Spirit

This is the condition of every Christian at all times. The Holy Spirit enters the life of a repentant sinner the moment he is saved and will dwell there permanently (**John 14:16; Romans 8:9**). This is also known as the "baptism of the Holy Spirit." In Greek (the primary language of the New Testament), to *baptize* means "to dip, immerse or submerge," and carries with it the idea of "being immersed into a new environment." When we are "baptized in (or with) the Holy Spirit," we are brought into the new environment or sphere of influence of the Spirit forever (**1 Corinthians 12:13**).

Filled by the Holy Spirit

This is the condition of a Christian who has submitted his will to the will of God, inviting the Holy Spirit to direct and empower his life. This filling is not a one-time experience, nor is the condition usually permanent. Filling may occur frequently—even daily or hourly—depending upon the initiative, obedience and consistency of the Christian (**Ephesians 5:18**). When a believer is not "filled," the Holy Spirit is no less present, but is less active or responsive, due to the disinterest or rebellious attitude of the believer. The remedy for this "unfilled" state is the focus of this study.

Who Is The Holy Spirit?

Third Person of the Trinity
...What? Are there THREE Gods or ONE?

We'll learn more about the nature of God in later studies, but it would be helpful to know a little more about the Holy Spirit right now in order to understand His ministry.

The Bible describes God as a "Trinity." In other words, one God manifesting Himself in three forms: the Father, the Son, and the Holy Spirit.

Read **John 6:27**. In this verse, Jesus spoke of _____ the Father.

Read **John 20:26-28**. Here, Thomas called Jesus "my Lord and my _____."

Read **1 Corinthians 3:16**. Christians are temples indwelt by the Spirit of _____.

Paradox! The Heavenly Father, Jesus Christ the Son, and the Holy Spirit are each referred to as God, and yet there is only ONE God:

"Before Me no god was formed, nor will there be one after Me." —**Isaiah 43:10b**	"Now this is eternal life: that they may know You, the only true God..." —**John 17:3a**	"... There is no God but one." —**1 Corinthians 8:4b**	"Hear, O Israel: The LORD our God, the LORD is one." —**Deuteronomy 6:4**

A paradox is a concept that seems to be self-contradictory and yet is true. For example, physicists tell us that light is both a particle and a wave, and yet other physical laws assert that it *can't* be both. Scientists will probably be able to explain this to us in logical terms some day, but until then, it's beyond our ability to comprehend—a paradox!

There are many things about God that are also beyond our ability to comprehend. After all, He is infinite, and we are quite limited in our brainpower compared to Him. Could you imagine trying to explain the workings of an electric motor to an ant? The ant would have virtually no frame of reference to your explanation! In the same way, there are many things about God that we'll never be able to completely grasp this side of heaven. The concept of the Trinity is one of them!

Nevertheless, God's Word—the Bible—asserts there is only one God, but He is manifested in three persons. Each has a different role and purpose. Sometimes all three are seen in the same event or talked about together. Examine the following four passages. Circle the three members of the Trinity mentioned in each one and draw a line to the label on the right side.

When Jesus issued the Great Commission:	⊙ **Father**
"Therefore go and make disciples of all nations, baptizing them in the name of the Father and of the Son and of the Holy Spirit." —**Matthew 28:19**	⊙ **Son** ⊙ **Holy Spirit**

When Mary learned she was going to give birth to Jesus:	⊙ **Father**
"The angel answered, 'The Holy Spirit will come upon you, and the power of the Most High will overshadow you. So the Holy One to be born will be called the Son of God.'" —**Luke 1:35**	⊙ **Son** ⊙ **Holy Spirit**

When Jesus was baptized by John the Baptist:	⊙ **Father**
"When all the people were being baptized, Jesus was baptized too. And as He was praying, heaven was opened and the Holy Spirit descended on Him in bodily form like a dove. And a voice came from heaven: 'You are My Son, whom I love; with You I am well pleased.'" —**Luke 3:21-22**	⊙ **Son** ⊙ **Holy Spirit**

Peter writing about God's work in Christians' lives:	⊙ **Father**
"… who have been chosen according to the foreknowledge of God the Father, through the sanctifying work of the Spirit, for obedience to Jesus Christ and sprinkling by His blood." —**1 Peter 1:2**	⊙ **Son** ⊙ **Holy Spirit**

Why Did The Holy Spirit Come?

Study the following Bible verses and write down what you think each is saying about why the Holy Spirit came, what His function is, what His plans are, etc. Feel free to also look up the passages in your Bible, in order to study the context in which each is found.

The Holy Spirit came to …

Jesus speaking of the Holy Spirit: "And when He has come He will convince the world of its sin, and of the availability of God's goodness, and of deliverance from judgment." —**John 16:8** [TLB] ⇒

Jesus speaking: "But when He, the Spirit of truth, comes, He will guide you into all truth." —**John 16:13** ⇒

Jesus speaking of the Holy Spirit: "He shall glorify Me; for He shall take of Mine, and shall disclose it to you." —**John 16:14** [NAS] ⇒

Jesus speaking: " 'If a man is thirsty, let him come to Me and drink. Whoever believes in Me, as the Scripture has said, streams of living water will flow from within him.' By this He meant the Spirit, whom those who believed in Him were later to receive." —**John 7:37-40** ⇒

The resurrected Jesus speaking: "But you will receive power when the Holy Spirit comes on you; and you will be My witnesses in Jerusalem, and in all Judea and Samaria, and to the ends of the earth." —**Acts 1:8** ⇒

Here's what the Holy Spirit has already done in your life since you became a Christian . . .

Entered you. At the moment you asked Jesus Christ to come into your life, He *did*—in the form of His Holy Spirit. See **1 Corinthians 3:16-17**.

Baptized you. You were immersed into the Kingdom of God, plunged into the new environment of God's Spirit, and incorporated into the spiritual body of Christ—His church. See **1 Corinthians 12:13**.

Sealed you. God affixed His eternal "signature" on you, testifying that you belong to Him forever, and that He will personally see to it that you are delivered safely to heaven at the end of your life. See **Ephesians 1:13-14**.

Gifted you. He gives every Christian one or more spiritual gifts, which will enable him or her to have a unique, fruitful, fulfilling ministry to both Christians and non-Christians. See **1 Corinthians 12:4-11**.

Empowered you. God's Spirit has given you supernatural ability to boldly communicate the Gospel to others in ways that will make sense and win them to His Kingdom both locally and around the world. See **Acts 1:8** and **Acts 4:31**.

Targeted you for blessing. Even now the Holy Spirit is actually praying to God the Father on your behalf. And one thing's for sure: the Holy Spirit really gets results when *He* prays! See **Romans 8:26-27**.

Here's what the Holy Spirit wants to do next...

Read the following passages in your Bible and describe some of the things the Holy Spirit would like to do for you on an on-going basis.

John 14:26 —	2 Corinthians 3:18 —	Galatians 5:22-23 —

The FILLING Of The Holy Spirit

When you are in the "filled" state, the lines of communication between you and God will be strong and clear, enabling Him to direct and empower you more effectively. But you may be wondering, "Why do I need *more* of God in my life?" It's not that you need more of Him; it's that He wants more of *you!* And neither you nor He will be satisfied until He has all of you and is Lord of every area of your life.

But even though God now lives within you in the form of His Holy Spirit, you still have a "free will." You can choose to obey God or to disobey Him. When you choose the latter, He won't play the autocratic dictator and force you into obedience (though He *will* allow you to suffer the consequences of your poor choices!). God's goal isn't an army of robots, but sons and daughters who can think and act righteously, and thus co-labor with Him in His eternal kingdom.

God has put His Holy Spirit right inside of us to help us make those right choices. When we turn a deaf ear to His promptings, the Bible says we "quench" the Holy Spirit (**1 Thessalonians 5:19**). How do you think this is like "quenching" a campfire?

The Bible also says we can "grieve" the Holy Spirit through our disobedience (**Ephesians 4:30**). What do you think this means?

If we truly want to nurture a loving and beneficial relationship with God, we need to respond positively to His gracious and merciful instructions—for our own good!

How do we know that being filled with the Holy Spirit requires a willful decision on our part and is not automatic?

In **Ephesians 5:18**, we are given two commands—one negative and one positive. What are they?

1. _____

2. _____

If something is **automatic**, do any commands need to be issued for it to happen?

If something is **commanded**, can we assume that if the command is not obeyed, the desired behavior might not occur?

Are we able to ignore the command not to get drunk?

Does it follow that we can also ignore the command to "be filled with the Spirit"?

What does it mean to be "filled" with the Holy Spirit?

How does alcohol alter a person's behavior?

Contrast this with how the Holy Spirit wants to alter a person's behavior.

Three Kinds Of People

Circle each of the three kinds of people spoken of in **1 Corinthians 2:14-15** and **3:1-3** [NKJV].

> "The natural man does not receive the things of the Spirit of God, for they are foolishness to him, nor can he know them, because they are spiritually discerned. But he who is spiritual judges all things … And I, brethren, could not speak to you as to spiritual people, but as to carnal, as to babes in Christ. I fed you with milk and not with solid food; for until now you were not able to receive it, and even now you are still not able; for you are still carnal."

The following diagrams can represent these three "classifications" of people:[3]

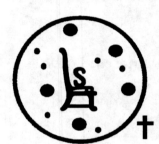

The Natural Man – "Captain of my own soul!"

S = Self, sitting on the throne or control center of his life.
✝ = Christ, outside the life.
Circles = Activities, interests, priorities and plans in discord.

This represents the **non-Christian**. As he tries to direct his own life in his finite and usually self-interested way, it often results in frustration, despair and discord with God's perfect plans for him.

The Spiritual Man – "Walking by faith."

S = Self dethroned, yielding to Christ's Lordship in his life.
✝ = Christ on the throne, guiding and empowering the Christian.
Circles = Activities, interests, priorities and plans in harmony!

This represents a **Spirit-filled Christian**. Since Christ is all-powerful and all-knowing, He can ensure the Christian's life will harmonize with God's plans for him, resulting in love, joy, peace patience, kindness, goodness, faithfulness, gentleness, and self-control—among other things!

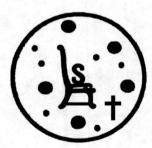

The Carnal Man –"I'll take it from here, thanks."

S = Self back on the throne, trying to direct his life again.
✝ = Christ still in the life, but dethroned and not allowed to be Lord.
Circles = Activities, interests, priorities and plans in discord.

This represents a **Carnal Christian**. As he ignores or disobeys God's directions, his life falls into disarray. Comparing frustration levels, dead-ends and despair, it's difficult to tell the difference between the Carnal Christian's life and the non-Christian's life.

Five Steps To Filling

1 Desire. Read **Matthew 5:6**. What does Jesus say is required in order to be "filled"?

What would this "desire" look like in your life?

> Search your heart. Do you "hunger and thirst for righteousness"? Do you truly *want* Jesus Christ as your Lord and the Holy Spirit as your Guide? Are you willing to obey what God tells you to do? Don't expect His power to flow unhindered if you're simply "going through the motions." God looks at the heart.

2 Confess. Read **1 John 1:9**. What does it say is required in order to be purified from all unrighteousness?

> The reason the Holy Spirit may be "quenched" in your life is because of sin – saying "No" to God and "Yes" to your unrighteous desires. In prayer, ask God to reveal the sins that have been "disconnecting" you from His plan and power. As He brings them to mind, agree with Him that those choices were wrong (which is the essence of confession). Ask Him to forgive you for each one.

3 Yield. Read **Romans 6:13,19**. The "yielding" (or offering or presenting) of ourselves spoken of in these two verses—does it involve a passive attitude or a purposeful commitment?

Verse 19 says when you "yield" yourself to God, you become a "slave" to righteousness. Describe what you think this means.

> Most people associate slavery with demeaning oppression—and in most cases, it is, but not in this case. In the spiritual realm, Satan desires to enslave you to his will which will lead to destruction. But God wants you to be enslaved to *His* will. This will lead to freedom from the things that tear you down and a strong connection to the things that will build you up and bring you satisfaction, fulfillment and joy.

4 Ask. Read **Luke 11:9-13**. What astounding, super-human exploits does this passage say you need to accomplish in order to "persuade" God to give you what you need?

Apparently, God *loves* to give us good gifts. Why do you think He requires us to "ask, seek and knock"? Why isn't His giving automatic and continual?

> Remember what was said earlier about our free will? God won't compromise your privilege of choosing. Since you made a willful choice to depart from His will, you need to make a willful choice to get "reconnected."

"Your body is now the dwelling place of the Third Person of the Trinity. Do not ask Him to help you as you would a servant. Ask Him to come in and do it all. Ask Him to take over in your life. Tell Him how weak, helpless, unstable, and unreliable you are. Stand aside and let Him take over in all the choices and decisions of your life."

–Billy Graham

"We are not going to move this world by criticism of it nor conformity to it, but by the combustion within it of lives ignited by the Spirit of God."

–Vance Havner

Promise:
"This is the confidence which we have before Him, that, if we ask anything according to His will, He hears us. And if we know that He hears us in whatever we ask, we know that we have the requests which we have asked from Him."
—1 John 5:14-15
[NAS]

Command:
"Do not get drunk on wine, which leads to debauchery. Instead, be filled with the Spirit."
—Ephesians 5:18

5 Thank Him in Faith.

Read **Mark 11:24** and notice the past tense used. What does this verse say will happen if you believe that you have received what you desired?

If you ask for something and believe you have received it, the normal thing to do next would be to say thank you! How can you be so sure that you now have been filled by the Holy Spirit?

What is the **promise** found in the verse on the left, **1 John 5:14-15**?

Why might one think being filled with His Holy Spirit would be according to God's will?

Would God **command** you to do something that was outside of His will? Obviously not! So based on God's **promise** and His **command**, you can have complete faith that if you've asked Him to fill you—and truly meant it—you *are* filled. He wants it, you want it, done deal!

Asking To Be Filled

When you ask or pray, God isn't as concerned with your words as He is with the attitude of your heart. But sometimes it helps to express what's in your heart if someone else supplies the words for you. Here is a suggested prayer:

> *Dear Father, I need You. I hunger and thirst for Your righteousness, rather than for the rags of the world. I want You to be my Master and my Guide. But I confess I have taken the throne of my life from Your control and have sinned against You. I've made many wrong choices. Please forgive me for this. I yield myself to You in obedience, desiring to serve You, rather than myself or my enemy, the Devil. I ask You to fill me with Your Holy Spirit. I step down from the throne of my life and give it back to You. I have faith that, based on Your command and Your promise, You have heard my prayer and have filled me with Your Holy Spirit. Thank you! Amen.*

Does this prayer express what you'd like to say to God? If so, take time right now and pray it to Him.

How To Know You're Filled

Your main assurance should be based in FAITH. God desires that we live by faith, and not always depend on evidence gathered through our five senses. If you truly desired His filling, confessed your sin, yielded, asked and thanked Him in faith, you can have complete confidence that He heard your prayer and granted your request—because we know it's right in line with His will.

Most transformations in the spiritual realm will eventually be manifested or make a difference in the material realm. What are some things you should begin to observe which would verify your filling? Read on for some ideas …

The Acts Of The Apostles

The Holy Spirit was very active in the newly formed church after Christ's resurrection. Many fillings were noted. Various actions and attitudes were seen immediately after each filling—depending on what was needed at the moment. Read each passage below in your Bible and write down what happened after the Holy Spirit filled someone.

Acts 2:1-11 _____

Acts 4:8-13 (hint: Peter's attitude?) _____

Acts 4:31 _____

Acts 7:54-56 _____

Acts 9:17-18 _____

The previous passages in Acts describe some pretty miraculous results of being filled, but His effect on us may not always be so dramatic! What does each of the following passages say will occur in those who are directed and empowered by the Holy Spirit?

Luke 4:1 _____

Luke 4:18-19 _____

John 16:13 _____

Galatians 5:22-23 _____

Romans 8:5-8 _____

Once filled, always filled?

It's a natural part of the human condition for us to periodically re-take the throne of our lives by asserting our will and ignoring God's will. As we grow spiritually, our objective is for this to happen less and less! In the meantime, we must be prepared to recognize when we have slipped into the "carnal" category and take measures to once again be Spirit-filled. Remember: this doesn't mean we are no longer saved, or that the Holy Spirit has left us. It simply means we've pushed Jesus Christ off the throne of our life and are trying to run things ourselves.

A literal translation from the original Greek text of **Ephesians 5:18** would be "Be being filled with the Holy Spirit." Notice that it's not a once-and-for-all experience—it's describing an on-going condition that we are to seek to maintain. It's like being commanded, "Keep that candle lit!" When it gets blown out, we simply need to re-light it.

Spiritual Breathing

Here is an illustration that will help you understand what to do when you need to be "re-filled." Think of it in terms of breathing. When you exhale, you rid your body of harmful carbon dioxide. When you inhale, you draw life-giving oxygen back into your body. Out with the bad, in with the good. A similar thing happens in the realm of the Spirit.

Exhale. When you become aware of sin in your life, it's time to take a spiritual breath. First, you must exhale by **confessing** your sin. The Greek word for "confession" is *homologeo,* which means "to say the same thing as." God's Spirit tells you your action was wrong, and you agree with Him—that's confession. And if you truly agree with Him about it, you'll not only say so, you'll quit doing the thing that was grieving Him. That's what **"repentance"** is: "to stop, turn around, and go back the other way." Do you remember the promise of **1 John 1:9**?

Inhale. Now breathe in the life of the Holy Spirit by asking Him to once again take the throne of your life. By faith, allow Him to control, empower and guide you. When you make this request, you can *know* He will immediately grant it based on His command in **Ephesians 5:18** and His promise in **1 John 5:14-15**.

How often do I do this?

As often as you need to do it. It may be once a week, once a day, once an hour or even once every few minutes! The important thing is to not lose heart and give up in defeat. As a drowning man will struggle frantically to clear his lungs of water and breathe in oxygen, so we need to recognize the critical need to keep the Holy Spirit on the throne of our lives—confessing our sins and seeking His filling.

Spiritual breathing should become as natural and automatic as our physical breathing. Each time you sense the conviction of the Holy Spirit, stop right then and take a spiritual breath. Some Christians have adopted the habit of starting out each day—even before getting out of bed— asking God if there is anything in them that is displeasing to Him, confessing anything that He reveals, and then asking Him to fill them with His Holy Spirit.

Personal Application:

If you have not been experiencing the Spirit-filled life lately, why not? What do you plan to do about it?

Can you remember the last time you were convicted of a particular sin by God, confessed it, repented, and asked Him to fill you with His Holy Spirit? If it's been a while, perhaps now would be a good time to spend some time before His throne of grace and seek His filling.

❑ I did this today. Date: _____ Notice any immediate results?

_____

❑ I don't need to at this time—I've been living controlled by the Spirit pretty consistently lately.

❑ Frankly, I don't understand the concept or see the need.

Scripture Memory Verse:

The Power Connection—
"Do not get drunk on wine, which leads to debauchery. Instead, be filled with the Spirit."
—**Ephesians 5:18**

[1] *Encyclopedia Of 7,700 Illustrations*, edited by Paul Lee Tan (Hong Kong: Nordica Int'l, Ltd, 1979), p. 1403.
[2] Vine, W.E. *An Expository Dictionary of New Testament Words* (Old Tappan, NJ; Revell, 1940, 1966), Vol. 1, p. 169.
[3] Bright, William R., *Have You Made the Wonderful Discovery of the Spirit-Filled Life?* (Orlando, FL: Campus Crusade for Christ, 1966, 1995). Illustration used by permission.

The Victory Connection...
...Neglecting Your Old Nature

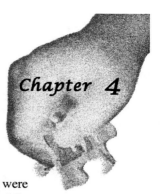

Chapter 4

Why Make This Connection?

A young teenager and his grandfather were fishing one warm summer morning. The two were quite close and often discussed the deeper issues of life. The old man had walked with the Lord for more than half a century; the teen had been a Christian for only a few years. Their respect for each other was obvious.

"Grandpa," the teenager said on this particular morning, "I've got a problem I wonder if you might help me out with."

"Well, I'll try. What is it, son?"

"It's this 'Christian' thing. I know that I should be living a better life – one that's more obedient to God and all. And sometimes I do pretty good at it. But sometimes I don't. I find myself acting like a lot of my non-Christian friends, getting mad at my sister for no good reason, doing things that I know are wrong… why can't I be good *all* the time?"

The Grandfather cast his line out toward the middle of the lake. "I know just what you're talking about." He paused for a moment, studying where his lure plopped. "You wanna know something? Don't tell anybody this, but sometimes I have the same problem you're describing."

"Really?" the teen asked, incredulously. "But you – you're Grandpa! How could *you* – I mean, I can't believe *you* would have problems being good."

Grandpa chuckled. "Oh, you can believe it, boy. It's nowhere near as bad as it used to be. But there are times when it seems like I've got two dogs inside of me – a good one and a bad one – both fighting to be 'top dog' in my life."

"Hey! I feel just like that, too! Two dogs fighting inside… which one wins with you, Gramps?"

The wise, old man began reeling in his line, looked sideways at the boy with a twinkle in his eye, and replied, "The one I feed, son."

The Fight

Can you identify with this "fight"? Most Christians can. Even the Apostle Paul struggled with it, writing in **Romans 7:18-19**…

> "I know that nothing good lives in me, that is, in my sinful nature. For I have the desire to do what is good, but I cannot carry it out. For what I do is not the good I want to do; no, the evil I do not want to do—this I keep doing."
>
> **—Romans 7:18-19**

By now, you have probably heard several times that – if you've invited Christ to be your Savior – you are a "new creation" (**2 Corinthians 5:17**). But if that's the case, why do you still find yourself struggling with many of your same "old creation" sins?

As was pointed out in the story, it all goes back to which dog you feed. Read on to find out more about the source of the struggle and how to be victorious in it.

Prayer Seed:
"Father, I'm tired of struggling. I long to be Your obedient child, to please You in every way - but I fail so often. Please teach me how to walk with You in consistent victory. Amen."

"Gradually it was disclosed to me that the line separating good and evil passes not through states, nor between classes, nor between political parties – but right through every human heart – and all human hearts."

–Alexander Solzhenitsyn in Gulag Archipelago

In With The New, Out With The Old?

When you received Christ, you were immediately indwelt by the Holy Spirit. What this means is that you inherited infinite supernatural power that would enable you live a life that would be pleasing to God, helpful to those around you and satisfying to you.

On a scale of 1 to 10, to what degree are you *actually experiencing* this? _____

1=hardly ever
10=all the time

If you wrote down "10" congratulations! Now, don't change a thing! You're one of the incredibly miniscule few who have already figured out the secrets of living a victorious and fruitful life (or else you're in *serious* denial!). But if you're like most growing Christians, you are still in need of further help in this area.

Study the following passage written by the Apostle Paul – who was most assuredly a Spirit-filled, Christ-loving, God-honoring man, and yet still had his struggles:

> "It seems to be a fact of life that when I want to do what is right, I inevitably do what is wrong. I love to do God's will so far as my new nature is concerned; but there is something else deep within me, in my lower nature, that is at war with my mind and wins the fight and makes me a slave to the sin that is still within me. In my mind I want to be God's willing servant but instead I find myself still enslaved to sin. So you see how it is: my new life tells me to do right, but the old nature that is still inside me loves to sin. Oh, what a terrible predicament I'm in! Who will free me from my slavery to this deadly lower nature?"
> —**Romans 7:21-24** [TLB]

Key Observation: One of the main facts that we should note from this passage in Romans 7 is that, though we now have a "new nature" as redeemed sons and daughters of God, we are still in full possession of our "old nature," and the two of them are constantly trying to gain the upper hand. When the new one came in, the old one didn't go out.

Paul describes two "natures" within himself, kind of like the "good dog" and the "bad dog" in our opening story. What terms does he use for these two natures?

"Good dog" = my _____ nature, or my _____ life.

"Bad dog" = my _____ nature, or my _____ nature.

What does Paul's new nature love to do?

What does Paul's old nature love to do?

To what degree can you identify with Paul's experience? _____

1=hardly ever
10=all the time

We truly **want** to change; we **want** to be obedient to God, but we often just seem to lack the power. As you learned in Chapter 3, the Holy Spirit is our power source. When He is on the throne of our lives, we **will** experience power, victory and the abundant life. But the daily – even moment-by-moment – challenge lies in keeping "Self" *off* the throne and keeping Christ *on* it.

But – whether or not you realize it – we Christians often ask ourselves . . .

Why Should I?

"Why should I *want* the Holy Spirit controlling my life? I mean, before I became a Christian *I* was in the driver's seat. That was 'normal'. I was *used to* calling all the shots. Some of my sins were pretty fun, and frankly, they still are. Now, I admit that I hate the consequences; I hate how they make me feel; I hate how they grieve God; I hate how Satan laughs every time I fall … But I still love to sin – if I didn't love it, I wouldn't keep doing it! So why would I want the Holy Spirit in charge of my life, spoiling all my fun?"

What do you think? How would you answer the question presented on the previous page?

With every temptation, we are given a choice: we can go God's way, or we can go Satan's way. If we know where we are going and really want to get there, a fork in the road doesn't present much of a problem. But for most of us, we have chosen the alternative Satan has offered us so often it's become a habit. As illogical and unsatisfactory as it's always been, we're just so *used* to agreeing to his hollow suggestions that we hardly even think about what God is offering us.

Our enemy contributes to this dangerous situation by deceiving us into thinking that going God's way won't produce satisfying results anyway – but his would. "I'll meet your needs, give you what you want, set you free, whatever – and it won't hardly cost you a thing," Satan purrs. "But God is just a cosmic spoil-sport. He only wants to tie you up, limit your fun, and hold you back. Choose my way!" He makes it sound so good. So when we nibble at the bait, he sets the hook.

If you understand the tension that exists between our old nature and our new nature, and how the filling of the Holy Spirit and *making right choices* combine to give us victory, you can experience major, sustained triumph in your day-to-day walk with the Lord.

Your life before Christ

The way you were, before you received Christ, could be represented by the farm in our parable. The farmer represents your **mind** – the part of you that makes decisions. The underground stream represents your **old nature**, and the contamination represents your **sinfulness**. The well represents the **attitudes and behaviors** that our old nature produces.

As the farmer only had one contaminated well to draw from, and wasn't aware of the contamination, so we only had one contaminated nature to draw on.

Read **Mark 7:14-23** in your Bible. What does it say about the source of sinfulness in our lives?

The Parable of the Two Wells

Once upon a time, there was a farmer who had been born and raised on a certain farm. He eventually inherited the farm from his parents, and now he was raising his family there.

The farmer and his family always seemed to be weak and sick. They didn't know it, but the well — which had been located right next to their farmhouse and serviced their farm for decades — was contaminated. The underground stream that fed the well went under an old, toxic waste dump, and every time they took a drink from it, the contamination hurt them a little bit more. Since the farmer and his family had been drinking from that well for decades, they didn't even know they were sick — they thought everyone felt like they did.

[to be continued]

Additional Resource: "The Parable of the Two Wells" was developed from the graphical "Two Wells Illustration" reproduced in Appendix #3.

Observe the kinds of attitudes and behaviors that our "old well" produces:

"The acts of the sinful nature are obvious: sexual immorality, impurity and debauchery; idolatry and witchcraft; hatred, discord, jealousy, fits of rage, selfish ambition, dissensions, factions and envy; drunkenness, orgies, and the like."
—Galatians 5:19-21

> "As for you, you were dead in your transgressions and sins, in which you used to live when you followed the ways of this world and of the ruler of the kingdom of the air, the spirit who is now at work in those who are disobedient. All of us also lived among them at one time, gratifying the cravings of our sinful nature and following its desires and thoughts. Like the rest, we were by nature objects of wrath."
> —Ephesians 2:1-3

According to the passage to the left, how many of us Christians – before we knew Christ – drew our attitudes and behaviors from this contaminated sinful nature?

Was this set of attitudes and behaviors something we learned – something we had to consciously try to produce? Or did it come naturally?

OK, maybe we *were* pretty pathetic people in those days before being redeemed by our Savior. But not many of us were really, *really* bad. Not many were ax-murderers, rapists, or armed robbers. In fact, I'll bet that for many of us, our good deeds outweighed our bad ones. I mean, we were *trying* to do the right thing – most of the time. Wouldn't that earn us some points with God? To answer this question, look up **Isaiah 64:6** in your Bible and write the verse in your own words below.

Salvation!

This event in the farmer's life represents your salvation – the day you realized you needed a Savior and a new "water source" and took *action*. The new underground stream represents your **new nature**, and it has no contaminating sinfulness in it. The new well represents the **new attitudes and behaviors** that your new nature produces.

The Parable, continued...

One day, a man from the Environmental Protection Agency came by and tested the farmer's well. The farmer was alarmed to hear of the contamination, and of course, he immediately stopped using the well.

But farms, farmers and farmers' families need water. So he consulted with some well-digging experts who informed him that they were relatively certain there was another underground stream on the other side of his property, coming from another direction.

The farmer drilled a new well where the experts indicated, and sure enough, the water that came up was pure.

[to be continued]

Read **2 Corinthians 5:17**, a passage which, by now, you may be pretty familiar with. Fill in the missing blanks:

> "Therefore, if anyone is in Christ, he is a _____ creation. The old has gone, the _____ has come."

Galatians 5:22-23 talks about the kind of attitudes and behaviors that this new well produces:

> "But the fruit of the Spirit is love, joy, peace, patience, kindness, goodness, faithfulness, gentleness and self-control."

Since you became a Christian, are you seeing more of this fruit produced in your life? What do you think you could do to increase your "fruit-bearing"?

The new water from the new well set the farmer and his family free from the sickness and death of the old, contaminated well. What does **Romans 8:1-2** say *we* have been set free from?

What does this mean?

> "Therefore, there is now no condemnation for those who are in Christ Jesus, because through Christ Jesus the law of the Spirit of life set me free from the law of sin and death."
> —**Romans 8:1-2**

The following passages tell us about the **true nature** of the new believer. In each passage, circle any terms that describe the "New You."

> "By one sacrifice He has made perfect forever those who are being made holy."
> —**Hebrews 10:14**
>
> "And by [God's] will, we have been made holy through the sacrifice of the body of Jesus Christ once for all."
> —**Hebrews 10:10**
>
> "For those God foreknew [that is, people He knew in advance were going to receive His Son] He also predestined to be conformed to the likeness of His Son, that He might be the firstborn among many brothers. And those He predestined, He also called; those He called, He also justified; those He justified, He also glorified."
> —**Romans 8:29-30**

The "New Well" represents the "New You" – the REAL you. From now on you can truthfully say, "It's not *like* me to be dishonest or selfish. It's not *like* me to be lustful or proud. The *real* me is characterized by love, joy, peace, patience, kindness, goodness, faithfulness, gentleness and self-control!"

However...

Almost immediately we notice a problem. Sometimes we're *not* loving. Sometimes we're *not* joyful. How is it, if we Christians have this "new nature" within us, we still sin?

Just as the farmer's old, contaminated well still sits right next to his house, so our old nature still exists within us. Not only is it accessible, it is probably *more* accessible than our new nature, because for so many years, it's all we had to draw from. We're *used* to going there to get our needs met.

Why might the farmer continue to drink from the old well rather than from the new one?

> *The Parable,* continued...
> The health of the farmer and his family began to gradually improve after they had stopped drinking from the contaminated well and started drinking the pure water of the new well.
> But their troubles were not over. The main problem: the old well remained right next to the farmhouse, but the new well was a good quarter-mile away. To get to it a person had to follow a narrow path up and over a hill, past a wolverine den, and right next to a briar patch. They couldn't afford plumbing, and it wasn't always convenient to draw water from the new well.
> [to be continued]

Chapter 4 - The Victory Connection **29**

The Ministry of the Holy Spirit

Think About It: In what ways do the following issues explain why the farmer continues to drink from a well that he knows is contaminated? How does each relate to why Christians continue to draw their attitudes and behaviors from their old nature?
-Rationalization
-Doubt
-Arrogance
-Laziness
-Habit

Remember that for most of his life, everytime the farmer was thirsty he would go out his farmhouse door, turn left, and walk those few yards down the path to his well. It's going to take him awhile to alter his response to his thirst, turn *right,* and walk the path to the new well.

The Holy Spirit is like a giant neon sign that is now planted right outside the farmer's door. Everytime he comes outside for some water, the sign flashes, TURN RIGHT!!!

Unfortunately, the farmer can choose to *ignore* the sign. In the same way, you can choose to ignore the promptings of the Holy Spirit. That's why, ultimately, it's going to be up to *you* to decide which "well" to use. God will help you, but you must make the decision.

According to the passage on the right, what are we to "put off" and what are we to "put on"?

> "You were taught, with regard to your former way of life, to put off your old self, which is being corrupted by its deceitful desires; to be made new in the attitude of your minds; and to put on the new self, created to be like God in true righteousness and holiness."
> —**Ephesians 4:22-24**

Check the sentence that you think is correct:

- ❑ This "putting off" and "putting on" is a passive thing that happens to me automatically.

- ❑ This "putting off" and "putting on" requires an act of my will—conscious choices on my part.

Study **Romans 12:1-2**:

> "Therefore I urge you, brothers, in view of God's mercy, to offer your bodies as living sacrifices, holy and pleasing to God – which is your spiritual worship. Do not conform any longer to the pattern of this world, but be transformed by the renewing of your mind. Then you will be able to test and approve what God's will is – His good, pleasant and perfect will."
> —**Romans 12:1-2**

This passage issues three commands, one in verse 1, two in verse 2. What are they?

1. _____

2. _____

3. _____

What do you think the Apostle Paul – through the inspiration of the Holy Spirit – is talking about here when he says that we should "offer our bodies as living sacrifices" to God?

How can we stop being "conformed to the pattern of this world"?

Old Nature Thinking vs. God's Thinking:

"It's impossible."
All things are possible.
    –Luke 18:27

"I'm confused."
I will direct your path.
    –Proverbs 3:5-6

"I'm not able."
I am able.
    –2 Corinthians 9:8

"I'm not strong enough."
I will strengthen you.
    –Philippians 4:13

"I can't manage."
I will supply your needs.
    –Philippians 4:19

"It's too much for me."
I will help you.
    –Isaiah 41:10

"I'm worried."
I'll take your worries.
    –1 Peter 5:7

"I'm too tired."
I will give you rest.
    –Matthew 11:28-30

"It's not worth it."
It will be worth it.
    –Romans 8:28-30

"Nobody loves me."
I will always love you.
    –Romans 8:38-39

"I'm afraid."
I will give you peace.
    –Isaiah 26:3

Renewing Your Mind

The third command in **Romans 12:1-2** is that our minds should be "renewed." Our minds need to be re-taught to draw upon the supernatural resources of our new nature instead of the contaminated sewage of our old nature.

How do we do this? Here are two key strategies:

1 Consistent Filling Of The Holy Spirit

If the Holy Spirit has a "renewing" effect upon us, what does **Titus 3:5** tell you about the need to stay filled – controlled and empowered – by the Holy Spirit?

> "He saved us, not because of righteous things we had done, but because of His mercy. He saved us through the washing of rebirth and renewal by the Holy Spirit."
>
> —**Titus 3:5**

The Parable, continued...

The farmer and his family really *did* want to stop drinking from the old contaminated well, and as time passed, they noticed an interesting phenomenon regarding the paths to the wells. Every time they made the trip to the new well, its path was beaten down and smoothed out a little bit more – making it easier to find and more familiar to them. Meanwhile, the path to the old well became less passable and harder to find. It worked the other way, too. A trip to the old well made the next trip there easier, while the new well path became less desirable.

So the farmer and his family made a decision: even though it was harder, they would help each other to remember to use only the new well. Before long, they noticed three things: (1) they weren't weak and sick anymore, because the journey to the new well had become easier, (2) the path to the old well had become almost impossible to find, due to lack of use, and (3) it had now become a natural, unconscious habit to turn *right* instead of left as they left their farmhouse to get water.

2 Consistent Feeding On God's Word

Another word for this renewal process is "sanctification." Read what Jesus said about this sanctifying renewal in His prayer to His Father, in **John 17:17**.

> "Sanctify them by the truth; Your word is truth"
>
> —**John 17:17**

Extra Insight: "Sanctification" means to make holy, to purify, to set apart for sacred purposes.

If Jesus Christ has asked the Father to renew us through His Word, what does this tell you about the need to spend consistent time studying the Bible?

Here's where the choices come in...

List the three advantages the farmer and his family experienced as they consistently drew from the new well (in your own words):

1. _____

2. _____

3. _____

List three parallel advantages that the Christian will experience if he or she consistently chooses to walk in the Spirit and study and apply God's Word:

1. _____

2. _____

3. _____

Your choice... A country preacher once observed: "Brethren, it's like this: the Lord He is always voting *for* man, and the devil is always voting *against* him. Then the man himself votes and breaks the tie!"

The Key

Every time you **obey God** in the small, easy, "maintenance" type issues in your life, such as:

- Confessing your sins and repenting when the Holy Spirit convicts you
- Asking the Holy Spirit to fill you whenever you notice you've retaken the "throne"
- Reading and applying the Bible
- Going to church
- Praying

Repentance: a change of mind involving both a turning from sin and a turning to God.

… you are "renewing your mind," training it to draw on your new nature and to neglect your old nature, thereby strengthening and sanctifying the "New You."

Then, when the really critical, monstrous, life-and-death types of choices confront you, such as:

- Adultery
- Drugs
- Stealing
- Rejecting Christ
- Murder

… you will be strong, ready, and unable to find the path to the "old well." In fact, your first knee-jerk reaction will be to start sprinting down the path to the new well.

In short: every time you obey God, it makes it *easier* to obey Him again the next time. This all adds up to long-term, sustained VICTORY!

"The key to usefulness, to revelation, and to a Holy Spirit filled life is obedience to the Word of God."
–John G. Mitchell

Personal Applications:

1. Take some time to examine your heart. Better yet, ask the Lord to examine your heart and to tell you if there are any areas of your life in which you are being disobedient, drawing from "the old well," and not allowing Him to be on the throne of your life.

2. If He convicts you of something that needs to be confessed, repented of and surrendered to Him, do it now!

3. Ask the Lord to help you become quickly aware of it any time you start down the path to "the old well," and to help you turn around and go the other way.

4. Ask Him to help you remain filled with the Holy Spirit and obedient to Him.

5. Make a commitment to spend some time reading the Bible and praying each day – even if it's only for five or ten minutes.

6. Make a commitment to go to church regularly for fellowship with other Christians.

7. Make a commitment to tell others about Christ as God gives you opportunities.

WRAP UP
Jesus asks you, "Will you obey Me?"

Scripture Memory Verse:

The Victory Connection—
"Do not conform any longer to the pattern of this world, but be transformed by the renewing of your mind. Then you will be able to test and approve what God's will is – His good, pleasant and perfect will."

—**Romans 12:2**

The Growth Connection...
...Actions And Attitudes To Optimize Your Development

Chapter 5

Why Make This Connection?

Benvenuto Cellini, the great Italian sculptor, tells of a time when a massive block of marble was delivered to Florence, Italy. It was perfect except for one significant flaw. And because of this, no artist was even willing to submit a design for it – except one.

There was a public square in Florence where the block of marble was set. A tall fence was built around it, and a shack was erected for the artist. For two years the sculptor labored. Finally, the fence was torn down, the shack was taken away, and all of Florence was allowed to behold the result. They were awe-struck. Even today, many people consider this sculpture to be among the most magnificent ever created: Michelangelo's "David."[1]

In that solid block of marble was a glorious statue. Others couldn't see it, but Michelangelo did. Others rejected it because of its flaw, but Michelangelo knew right from the beginning how he was going to work around it.

God has been looking at you for a long, long time. And He, too, sees a glorious, finished product in your essence, even now. He knows all your flaws, but He also knows how to work around them – and even how to eliminate them. God's idea is to make you into a man or a woman who looks just like Jesus Christ – not physically of course, but spiritually – in your attitudes, your priorities, and the themes, rhythms and preferences of your life. He wants to work on you from the inside out and chip away the parts of you that don't conform to the image of Christ, while He accentuates, smoothes and polishes the parts that do.

A Monumental Difference...

There is an important point to remember here: you are not a chunk of cold, lifeless marble. Unlike the rock, you have the ability to squirm under the Sculptor's chisel. You can be uncooperative and opinionated about His plans. You can be uninterested in His objectives or bored and impatient with His progress. You might even get up on your half-chiseled legs and walk away from *His* public square and not show up for days or weeks at a time. You can even harden yourself – so much so that the blows of the Sculptor's hammer on His chisel don't seem to chip off even the tiniest fleck of stone. Ultimately, there you sit, month after month, year after year, decade after decade, a half-finished masterpiece.

The goal of this study is to help you learn how to avoid that "uncooperative" condition. In your heart, you *know* you want to change – to be made like Jesus Christ. The process isn't quick or easy, but there are some specific activities that you can engage in that will help you strap in for the long journey and actually hasten and enhance the process God has in mind for you.

This study will lay the foundation for the next four studies that follow it. By the time you've made your way through these five lessons, you should own some very practical insights that will set you up for a lifetime of growth, fruit-bearing and personal fulfillment.

Prayer Seed:
"Father, You have birthed me into the spiritual realm. In so many ways, I feel like a spiritual infant – but I don't want to stay like this! I want to feel comfortable and familiar in Your Kingdom. Help me grow up, Lord. Show me what I need to do to co-operate with You in this maturing process. Give me the wisdom, the insight, and the patience that is required. Amen."

Elements of Spiritual Growth

As with most things that grow, there are several factors that will contribute to your maturation as a new spiritual being. Here are six key elements:

1. **The Lordship of Christ**
2. **The Bible**
3. **Prayer**
4. **Fellowship**
5. **Witnessing**
6. **Obedience and Action**

If you are interested in the most efficient and effective growth experience, you won't rely on just one or two of these elements, but on a good mix of them all. To demonstrate how they work together to keep your life "rolling along toward maturity", this study – and the next four – will use the "Wheel Illustration"[2] as a guide. This is a classic teaching tool developed in the 1950's by Dawson Trotman, founder of The Navigators. It has helped hundreds of thousands of people gain an understanding of how they can cooperate with God's plans to help them grow. We'll build the Wheel as we work through this study.

1 The Lordship of Christ

In every wheel, the power begins in the hub, radiates out through the spokes and energizes the rim. As you can see in the Wheel on the left, in a Christian's life, the central power generator is Jesus Christ through the ministry of His Holy Spirit.

Chapter Three in this study (*The Power Connection*) focused on this key element, but let's expand on it a little here.

Look up each of the following verses in your Bible. **Write out what each of them says will happen** to a person who has Christ at the center of their life.

Matthew 6:33

How does one "seek first the Kingdom of God"?

John 12:26

What do you think it means to "follow" Jesus?

John 15:4-7

Extra Insight: Various translations use the word *abide, remain* or *continue* in **John 15:4-7.** Regardless, the meaning of the term in Greek (*meno*) is "to remain constant in relationship to." Or as J.B. Phillips puts it, the abider is: "the man who shares My life, and whose life I share…"[3]

It's one thing to ask Jesus Christ to be your Savior, but have you asked Him to be your *Lord*? If not, why not take a moment right now and settle that issue?

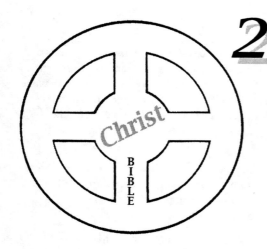

2 The Bible

As you learned in previous lessons, you are now a three-dimensional being composed of body, soul and spirit. You probably already know that groceries feed your body and that truth, beauty and good information feed your soul. What feeds your spirit – the part of you that relates to God? The Bible does! It is spiritual food for your New Nature.

What happens if a baby doesn't receive the milk it longs for (*besides* crying!)?

> "I believe the Bible is the best gift God has ever given to man. All the good from the Savior of the world is communicated to us through this book."
> –Abraham Lincoln

> "Like newborn babes, long for the pure milk of the Word, that by it you may grow in respect to salvation."
> —1 Peter 2:2

What do you think will happen to a young Christian who doesn't receive the "spiritual milk" that his spirit is craving?

The Effects of God's Word On Your Life

Examine each of the following scripture passages. **How does each one say you will benefit** as you spend time reading, discussing and applying the Bible?

> "Do not let this Book of the Law [*the Bible*] depart from your mouth [*keep talking about it!*]; meditate on it day and night, so that you may be careful to do everything written in it. Then you will be prosperous and successful." —**Joshua 1:8**

> "The law of his God is in his heart; his feet do not slip." —**Psalm 37:31**

> "How can a young man keep his way pure? By living according to Your word. I have hidden Your word in my heart that I might not sin against You." —**Psalm 119:9-11**

> "Your word is a lamp to my feet and a light for my path." —**Psalm 119:105**

> "If you remain in Me and My words remain in you, ask whatever you wish, and it will be given you." —**John 15:7**

> "All Scripture is God-breathed and is useful for teaching, rebuking, correcting and training in righteousness, so that the man of God may be thoroughly equipped for every good work." —**2 Timothy 3:16-17**

Read **John 8:31** in your Bible. What does this verse say is required of those who want to be considered disciples of Jesus Christ? What will happen for them if they meet this requirement?

3 *Prayer*

Do you know how much God loves you? He is totally enamored with you! As you sleep, He watches your face, counts the hairs on you head, and meditates on the plans He has for you! When you wake up each day, He can't wait to have fellowship with you. But remember – as in any relationship between two persons who love each other – communication is not only a joy, it's *vital* for the development of the relationship. It can't be one-way.

God wants to hear from you! He wants you to express your joys, your hopes, your fears, your questions, and your desires to Him. He wants to *commune* with you. That's what prayer is all about – a conversation between two people who love each other!

Read the following verses in your Bible. Each verse will present a reason why God *wants* us to talk to Him in prayer. Write down the reasons you observe in each verse.

Matthew 7:7-11

John 16:24

Philippians 4:6-7

> "Prayer is the greatest simplicity, speaking to Him frankly and plainly, and imploring His assistance in our affairs, just as they happen."
> –Brother Lawrence

> "Call to Me and I will answer you, and tell you great and unsearchable things you do not know."
> —Jeremiah 33:3

In the verse to the left, what benefit does God want to extend to you, if you will "call to" Him?

Is this a benefit that you are interested in? Why or why not?

PRAYER TYPES

There are four basic types of prayer. The four verses below are examples of each type. Read each verse and think of a word or phrase that describes each type. Example: "A prayer of confession."

> "I will exalt You, my God the King; I will praise Your name for ever and ever. Every day I will praise You and extol Your name forever and ever." —Psalm 145:1-2

> "For I know my transgressions, and my sin is always before me. Against You, You only, have I sinned and done what is evil in Your sight, so that You are proved right when You speak …" —Psalm 51:3-4

> "We give thanks to You, O God, we give thanks, for Your Name is near; men tell of Your wonderful deeds." —Psalm 75:1

> "Oh, that You would bless me, and enlarge my territory! Let Your hand be with me, and keep me from harm so that I will be free from pain." —1 Chronicles 4:10

Praise God for who He is – His *attributes;*
Thank God for what He has done – His *actions.*

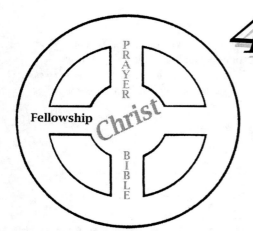

4 Fellowship

There are a number of analogies that God uses to teach us about the nature of His Kingdom. One of His favorites for describing the relationship that exists among His children is that of the members of a "body."

Find **1 Corinthians 12:4-26** in your Bible and read it. How are individual Christians like members of a body?

When a member of your physical body is hurt or needs help, what do the other members of your body do?

What does this tell you about how a local group of believers should act toward each other?

According to **Hebrews 3:13**, sin can do two things to you. First it D_____ you, and then it H_____ you. How would regular encouragement from other believers keep this from happening?

"But encourage one another daily, as long as it is called Today, so that none of you may be hardened by sin's deceitfulness."
—**Hebrews 3:13**

"As iron sharpens iron, so one man sharpens another..."
—**Proverbs 27:17**

According to **Proverbs 27:17**, what's another important benefit of spending time with other Christians?

Matthew 18:20 describes fellowship as "two or three coming together in My name." What special condition exists when this happens?

"For where two or three come together in My name, there am I with them."
—**Matthew 18:20**

How do you plan to fellowship?

- ❑ Sunday morning worship service
- ❑ Sunday evening worship service
- ❑ Some other weekly church meeting
- ❑ Small group Bible study
- ❑ Home fellowship group
- ❑ Prayer meeting
- ❑ One-to-one with my discipler
- ❑ On the golf course

- ❑ At the gym
- ❑ During a meal
- ❑ While running
- ❑ While shopping
- ❑ Riding a bike
- ❑ Camping
- ❑ While ministering
- ❑ At a sporting event

All of these settings can provide a wonderful environment for fellowship!

Think about it: The first positive characteristic required of an Elder (a church leader) in Titus 1:8 is "hospitality."

But please note: True, Biblical fellowship is more than just getting together and talking about the weather. Look for ways to encourage, build up, help, share scripture, provide positive corrective feedback, show love and let Jesus work *through you* to strengthen your friend!

PRAYER

BIBLE

Fellowship   *Christ*   Witnessing

5 Witnessing

What's the greatest thing that ever happened to you? If you're a Christian, you would probably say that becoming a Christian is, since that event opened the door to Christ and eternal life for you. If that's the case, what is the greatest thing you can do for another person?

> "Those who are wise will shine like the brightness of the heavens, and those who lead many to righteousness, like the stars forever and ever."
> —**Daniel 12:3**

Witnessing as lunch . . .

Find **John 4:1-34** and read it. This is an account of Jesus witnessing to a Samaritan woman at the well of Sychar. Normally, in those days, men would *never* stoop so low as to discuss theology with a *woman*, and no Jew would *ever* defile himself by speaking to a *Samaritan!* Yet Jesus rose above these social taboos and shared the gospel specifically and lovingly. The woman became a believer in Christ as the Messiah and ran to tell the rest of the town just as the disciples were returning with lunch for Jesus. When offered, Jesus politely refused – as though no longer hungry. In verses 32-34, Jesus tells what nourished Him even more than physical food. What was it?

Two Witnessing Methods:

These methods are two sides of the same coin; they go together. Don't use one without the other!

A. Your Life

> "No translation of the Bible is quite as effective as the flesh-and-blood edition."
> –**Vance Havner**

As the saying goes, "Your life is the only 'Bible' some people will read." Non-Christians may be reluctant to go to a church, or watch a Christian TV show, or read a gospel tract, but as they observe your Spirit-powered life at school, or at the office, or in the neighborhood, and as the Holy Spirit influences them through you, they will be intrigued and attracted by what they see in you. They'll want to know what makes you tick!

In the verse to the right it says that we are to let our "light shine before men." How do we do that?

> "Let your light shine before men, that they may see your good deeds and praise your Father in heaven."   —**Matthew 5:16**

But is simply doing good deeds enough? Don't people of other religions – even people of no religion – often live very good, caring, generous lives? What else is needed?

B. Your Words

> **Note:** You will be learning a method of verbally sharing the gospel in Chapter 9, *"The Witnessing Connection."*

People need to be drawn to the light of God that is in you, but once there, they need to *know* some pretty specific things in order to make a decision regarding Christ. This is where the *spoken* witness comes in. It's what Jesus was doing with the Samaritan woman at the well.

In **Romans 10:17**, what has to happen before faith can be born in a person?

> "Faith comes from hearing the message, and the message is heard through the word of Christ."   —**Romans 10:17**

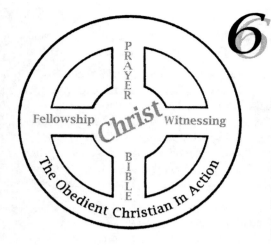

6 Obedience & Action

As God's enabling power moves from Christ at the center of a person's life through the spokes, it finally comes to the rim, ready to send the wheel rolling. But what if the rim is faulty? Without these two elements – *obedience,* which involves our will, and *action,* which carries out the decisions of the will – our wheel would remain stuck in a pothole. Become a Bible scholar if you like. Pray for hours at a time. Go to church whenever the doors are open. Witness to anything that moves. But if you're unwilling to respond obediently to God's specific promptings in His Word and through His Holy Spirit, don't expect to roll very far down the road to maturity.

What common theme do you notice in each of the verses to the right?

> "Whoever comes to Me, and hears My sayings and does them, I will show you whom he is like…" —**Luke 6:47** [NKJV]
> "My mother and My brothers are these who hear the word of God and do it." —**Luke 8:21** [NKJV]
> "More than that, blessed are those who hear the word of God and keep it!" —**Luke 11:28** [NKJV]
> "For not the hearers of the law are just in the sight of God, but the doers of the law will be justified." —**Romans 2:13** [NKJV]
> "But be doers of the word, and not hearers only, deceiving yourselves." —**James 1:22** [NKJV]

Find and read **Luke 6:46-49** in your Bible. Jesus shares this parable with a number of people who call Him their "Lord." But Jesus had a problem with this. What was it?

What dangerous habit will result in the "house" of your life collapsing when adversity hits?

According to **John 14:21** (verse to the right), how do we show our love for Jesus?

> "Whoever has My commands and obeys them, he is the one who loves Me. He who loves Me will be loved by My Father, and I too will love him and show Myself to him."
> —**John 14:21**

If we obey Christ, what will be God the Father's response? And what will be God the Son's two-fold response?

Three Other Important Factors . . .

The TIME Factor

Don't expect to become a "Super Christian" in just a few weeks or months – or even years. You'll need to be patient with yourself, with God, and with His program for you. Sometimes your progress may seem painfully slow, and you may wonder if there has been any progress at all. But God always takes His time when quality is involved. He'll take a hundred years to produce a decent oak tree, but a squash He can do in about two months.

> "To everything there is a season, a time for every purpose under heaven."
> —**Ecclesiastes 3:1**

There are no short cuts – no accelerated classes! And no growth process is uniform and perfectly paced. So as you experience exciting growth spurts and long periods of "status quo," remember it's all part of the process. As the tortoise told the hare: "Slow and steady wins the race."

> "When God develops character, He works on it throughout a lifetime. He's never in a hurry."
> –Charles Swindoll

The ADVERSITY Factor

Some Christians get confused when they experience difficult periods, reasoning that, "Since I'm a child of the King, He's supposed to make my road smooth and straight! What's wrong here?"

Have you ever looked at the rings of a tree under a microscope? You'll notice that the cells that make up the light-colored rings are big and fat. That's the summer growth, formed when there was plenty of water, nutrients and sunlight. Most trees will put on more girth in two months of summer than all the other months combined. But if you move your microscope over to the much-narrower dark rings, you'll notice the cells there are small, shriveled and thick-walled. This is the winter growth, formed when it was cold and dark, with much less food or water available. During the winter when it's toughest, a process called "solidification" goes on within the tree. If the tree didn't experience these periods of hardship, it would never be strong enough to withstand the storms that came its way.

It's the same way with our spiritual growth. God allows us to go through adversity, not because He can't help it, but because He knows it will make us stronger. It will prepare us for greater things to come.

As every athlete knows, "No pain – no gain!" Consider God as your heavenly coach, who will provide just the right amount of adversity to challenge, stretch and strengthen you!

The SOVEREIGNTY OF GOD Factor

Always remember that, since you asked God to be in control of your life, *He is!* He is more concerned about your spiritual development than even you are! He's planned it all out perfectly (**Jeremiah 29:11**). And if it sometimes looks a little chaotic, don't forget that anything that comes into your life from now on has been thoroughly screened by Him (**John 10:28-30**).

When I go to the dentist, I have virtually no idea what he's doing in my mouth. His rapturous discourses on bicuspids and amalgam baffle me. But I know *he* knows what's going on, so I can relax about it and let him work. Just so with God! He knows, so relax!

Personal Application:

Take an inventory of your personal "Wheel." If your life seems inordinately "bumpy" right now, it *could* be due to God's strength-training program for you – which is normal - or it could be because your wheel is out of whack. Is Christ at the "hub" of your life? Are all four "spokes" present and functional? Can you say with confidence that your rim is intact – you're obeying and acting on God's promptings? If not, ask God in prayer what you should do about it.

Scripture Memory Verse:

The Growth Connection—
"But seek first His kingdom and His righteousness, and all these things will be given to you as well."
—Matthew 6:33

[1] History from Donald Grey Barnhouse, *Let Me Illustrate* (Grand Rapids, MI: F. H. Revell, 1967), p. 353.
[2] "The Wheel Illustration," © 1976 by The Navigators. Used by permission of NavPress. All rights reserved.
[3] Phillips, J.B., *The New Testament in Modern English* (New York, NY: Macmillan, 1958), p. 214.

The Fellowship Connection...
...God Touching You Through Other Christians

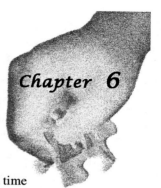

Chapter 6

Why make this connection?

Have you ever ventured to northern California and spent time walking among the majestic Redwood trees in the various parks there? These are the tallest and most massive trees on the planet, many of them ascending over 350 feet, and some are thought to be as old as 4,000 years. On quiet days, their groves seem like holy, ancient cathedrals. You might find yourself wishing they could talk, to pass on what it's like to have been alive since the days that Abraham, Isaac and Jacob walked the earth. What incredible strength, tenacity, and endurance they display to have weathered hundreds of winters and still stand so tall and magnificent!

But here's an interesting question for you: Have you ever seen a Redwood tree growing all by itself in the middle of a field? Probably not – unless the area around it was recently cleared by man. And if so, it won't stand there for long. God has ordained that Redwoods must always live in groves, because He is fully aware of their embarrassing secret: *shallow root systems.*

Unlike many trees that have deep taproots, Redwood root systems grow laterally and cover a huge area to efficiently absorb the rain that falls upon their often rocky habitations. So, in order to keep from being blown over, the Redwoods *interlace* their roots below the surface, forming a solid platform that stretches for acres. When the storms blow through their valleys, they remain standing because they hold each other up!

This is an excellent picture of what the Christian community is supposed to be like. The world can be a stormy place from time to time. A Christian who tries to "go it alone" is vulnerable, and it won't be long before he encounters difficulties that are more than he was designed to handle on his own. This is why it is necessary for Christians to get involved in each other's lives, interlace their "roots," and hold each other up during the storms that come along.

This is the essence of Christian Fellowship.

What Is Important To God?

As you may have noticed, the Bible is filled with laws, rules, commandments and ordinances. Is God some sort of a Cosmic Kill-joy, who wants to regulate our lives to death? Far from it. God is into being an excellent Father, and as such, He has been trying for centuries to help us grasp which things are good for us and which things will harm us. That's what His laws are all about.

But how is anybody supposed to *remember* all those laws, much less obey them? Jesus made it very easy for us. He told us that if we will completely follow just two commandments with our whole hearts, we will automatically be following all the other rules and regulations perfectly.

Read **Matthew 22:37-40** in your Bible. Write down the two commandments:

#1: _____

#2: _____

Prayer Seed:
"Thank You, Father, for including me in Your forever family. Help me to understand how I fit in, how I can help my brothers and sisters and be helped by them, and how we all work together to function as Your Body here on earth. Amen."

Extra Insight:
There are three Greek words for "love":
Eros: selfish love that desires to possess; erotic love.
Phileo: brotherly love; general fondness and affection.
Agapé: Godly, unselfish love – the kind of love Christians should have.[1]

Therefore, What Should Be Important To Us?

Since we will be spending the rest of our eternal lifetime with God in His kingdom, doesn't it make sense that we would want to adjust our priorities to line up with His? Function as we were designed? Become experts in the things He values?

If you agree with this, then you agree with the idea of becoming an *expert* at loving God and loving your fellow man – both Christians and non-Christians. The purpose of this study is to help you become excellent at loving your Christian brothers and sisters, and Chapter 9, *"The Witnessing Connection,"* will help you become equally adept at loving those who don't know Christ yet.

The Priority of Love In Christian Fellowship

"They are the true disciples of Christ, not who know most, but who love most."
–Fredrick Spanheim

Find **John 13:34-35** in your Bible. What did Jesus say would be a dead giveaway that His disciples were truly *His* disciples?

Jesus said that we were to love one another in the same way He loved us. What do you think He meant by this? What are some obvious characteristics of Jesus' love for us?

Write down one truth about Christian love that you observe in each of the following passages:

"If I have the gift of prophecy and can fathom all mysteries and all knowledge, and if I have a faith that can move mountains, but have not love, I am nothing."   **—1 Corinthians 13:2**

"Above all, love each other deeply, because love covers a multitude of sins."   **—1 Peter 4:8**

"Dear children, let us not love with words or tongue but with actions and in truth."   **—1 John 3:18**

"If anyone says, 'I love God,' yet hates his brother, he is a liar. For anyone who does not love his brother, whom he has seen, cannot love God, whom he has not seen."   **—1 John 4:20**

The "Other-Centeredness" of Christian Fellowship

"He works on us in all sorts of ways. But above all, He works on us through each other. Men are mirrors, or "carriers" of Christ to other men. Usually it is those who know Him that bring Him to others. That is why the church, the whole body of Christians showing Him to one another is so important."
–C. S. Lewis

To get a good idea about what Christians are supposed to *do* in relation to each other, examine the "one another" verses in the Bible (there are about 31 positive ones in the New Testament). Following is a sample of just six of them. Find each reference in your Bible and summarize what each one is directing us to do.

John 15:12 _____

Romans 12:10a _____

Romans 12:10b _____

Ephesians 4:2 _____

Ephesians 4:32 _____

Hebrews 10:25 _____

Which of the above "one another" verses do you think will give you the most trouble? Why?

What do you plan to do about it so that it won't be such a troublesome issue in the future?

What Qualifies as "True Fellowship"?

According to the following verses, what should happen when Christians fellowship?

"As iron sharpens iron, so one man sharpens another." —**Proverbs 27:17**	⇨
"Though one alone may be overpowered, two can defend themselves. A cord of three strands is not quickly broken." —**Ecclesiastes 4:12**	⇨
"They devoted themselves to the apostles' teaching and to the fellowship, to the breaking of bread and to prayer." —**Acts 2:42**	⇨
"We who are strong ought to bear with the failings of the weak and not to please ourselves. Each of us should please his neighbor for his good, and build him up." —**Romans 15:1**	⇨
"Speak to one another with psalms, hymns and spiritual songs. Sing and make music in your heart to the Lord." —**Ephesians 5:19**	⇨
"Let us consider how to stimulate one another to love and good deeds." —**Hebrews 10:24** [NAS]	⇨

We can't expect *each* of the above practices to occur *every time* Christians fellowship, but these things should be common and frequent. Given this, would the following scenarios qualify as true Christian fellowship?

1. Three Christian men get together for lunch and discuss the fortunes of their favorite baseball team, their latest computer upgrades, and the weather. ❑ YES ❑ NO

2. Three Christian women get together for an afternoon of cards, tea and discussions about *their* latest computer upgrades. ❑ YES ❑ NO

3. Two Christian couples get together for a competitive game of golf on a beautiful summer's day. ❑ YES ❑ NO

If you marked a "No" next to any of the preceding three scenarios, what would you add in each case to turn it into an encouraging time of true Christian fellowship?

1. _____

_____

2. _____

_____

3. _____

_____

What do you think? Can't Christians just get together and have fun without always trying to figure out how to make their social interaction times "qualify" as "true" Christian fellowship? [For a brief treatment of this, see the text box on the bottom of page 126.]

Where Does Fellowship Take Place?

Probably the first place that comes to our minds in answer to this question is **church!** It's a place specially designed for believers to gather on a regular basis in order to be encouraged and built up by other members of Christ's body, to be fed the Word of God, to worship God together, to pray together, and to get to know each other more deeply so that we can be better at "holding each other up" – like the Redwoods do.

The word "church" always refers to a collection of believers, but their numbers and their place of meeting may differ. Below, draw a line from each of the three verse boxes on the left to the box on the right that the word "church" is describing in each case.

Observed on a roadside billboard in Cleveland, OH: **"Let's meet at my house Sunday before the game. –God"**

"To the **church** of God in Corinth, to those sanctified in Christ Jesus and called to be holy…"
—**1 Corinthians 1:2**

- Refers generally to all Christian believers throughout the world.

"Aquila and Priscilla greet you warmly in the Lord, and so does the **church** that meets at their house."
—**1 Corinthians 16:19b**

- Refers to all Christian believers that live in a certain city.

[Paul speaking] "For I am the least of the apostles and do not even deserve to be called an apostle, because I persecuted the **church** of God."
—**1 Corinthians 15:9**

- Refers to a specific group of Christian believers that meet regularly in a particular place.

"We become like what we surround ourselves with. Show me your friends and I'll show you what you'll be like in ten years."
–Herb Evans
See also:
1 Corinthians 15:33

Clarification. Does a church have to be a permanent building with a steeple, painted white, with a cross somewhere prominently displayed? Churches often look like this, but in the days after Christ was crucified and resurrected churches met in people's homes, in Jewish synagogues, and sometimes out in the open. When the church began to be persecuted, they met in caves, out in the woods – even in tombs. Today we consider it a privilege to be able to meet in a beautiful building designated exclusively for church activities. But churches may also meet in homes, schools, storefronts, rodeo arenas, offices, gymnasiums, and restaurants. In Africa, they may meet under a tree for shade; in South America, under a tin shed to stay dry. Today, in places where Christians are persecuted, churches meet wherever they can be kept safe from the prying eyes of their tormentors. Remember: a church is the *people*, not the building!

Other Fellowshipping Contexts

Though a local church provides a foundational context for Biblical fellowship – and it is *definitely* to your advantage to be actively involved in one – fellowship can take place in a variety of venues. It doesn't have to be confined to an exclusive area within the four walls of a church building – or even to a scheduled meeting. Below, list four other places where you think you'd like to engage in some effective Biblical fellowship.

1. _____

2. _____

3. _____

4. _____

Characteristics of a Mature Fellowshipper

*Note: A list of these characteristics can be found in the margin of the Thought/ Discussion section for this chapter, page 127.

The Bible mentions at least twenty-six characteristics* of someone who has a mature grasp of Biblical fellowship. These are characteristics that should govern a person's relationships with other Christians at all times – not just on Sunday morning.

The following Bible passages highlight ten of these characteristics. In some cases, the scripture is supplied. In other cases, you'll need to find the passage in your Bible. Study each passage and write down one (or more) characteristic of a mature fellowshipper you find there.

Bible Passage	Characteristic(s)
Read **Mark 10:42-45** in your Bible.	
"Let us therefore make every effort to do what leads to peace and to mutual edification." —**Romans 14:19**	
"The Lord's servant must not quarrel; instead, he must be kind to everyone, able to teach, not resentful." —**2 Timothy 2:24**	
"Be devoted to one another in brotherly love. Honor one another above yourselves." —**Romans 12:10**	
"And when you stand praying, if you hold anything against anyone, forgive him, so that your Father in heaven may forgive you your sins." —**Mark 11:25**	
Read **1 Peter 5:5-6** in your Bible.	
"Everyone should be quick to listen, slow to speak and slow to become angry, for man's anger does not bring about the righteous life that God desires." —**James 1:19-20**	
Read **Matthew 5:43-48** in your Bible.	
"Share with God's people who are in need. Practice hospitality." —**Romans 12:13**	
"Rejoice with those who rejoice; mourn with those who mourn." —**Romans 12:15**	

On a positive attitude toward church attendance:
"Don't ever come to church without coming as though it were the first time, as though it could be the best time, and as though it might be the last time."
–Vance Havner

Dealing With Friction in the Fellowship

As someone once said, "If you ever find a perfect church, don't join it – you'll ruin it!" It is a fact that, even though the Lord Jesus Christ started the church, every one of them is made up of fallible humans. As Christians, they are loved by God, forgiven, redeemed from the enemy's hand and headed for heaven, but they're still humans. None of us is going to be perfect until they are with Christ in His eternal, glorified kingdom. The same is true of you, too!

In the mean time, you will need to *expect* occasional difficulties with other Christians. As Jesus said in **Matthew 9:12**, "It is not the healthy who need a doctor, but the sick." People who feel they are just fine without the Great Physician won't come to Him. But those who have recognized their needs and inadequacies seek Him out, just as a sick person goes to a doctor for help. So get used to it: your church is full of sick people! That didn't come out quite right... but I hope you get the point. Christians are forgiven – not perfect – and they are taking steps to get better (at least they've come to the hospital!). Here are some principles you can follow that will help both them and you get healthier whenever you find yourself at odds with another Christian.

1 Don't judge others.

One of the main reasons we are not to judge others is because we don't have enough information to *make* a valid judgment! Only one Person does: God – and we're not Him! So when we draw conclusions about another person's motives, character qualities, desires, words or actions, we're doing so with access to only a very small portion of the facts – and the likelihood is strong that we're wrong. God can see into a person's heart; humans can't. Leave the judging to God – you're main job is to love!

What would be the opposite of **judging** others?

> [Jesus speaking] "Do not judge, or you too will be judged. For in the same way you judge others, you will be judged, and with the measure you use, it will be measured to you."
> —**Matthew 7:1-2**

2 Check your own eye first.

People have a tendency to criticize others harshly and go easy on themselves. This is usually because if we can put someone else down, it makes us feel superior. You can see the devilishness in this, right? Instead, let's turn it around: look with critical discernment at your own shortcomings and go easy on others. Get your spiritual chainsaw, concentrate on the "tree" in your own eye, and join the "Loggers For Christ" club!

Can you think of any "planks" that need to be removed from your eye? Which do you plan to work on first?

> [Jesus speaking] "Why do you look at the speck of sawdust in your brother's eye and pay no attention to the plank in your own eye? How can you say to your brother, "Let me take the speck out of your eye," when all the time there is a plank in your own eye? You hypocrite, first take the plank out of your own eye, and then you will see clearly to remove the speck from your brother's eye."
> —**Matthew 7:3-5**

3 Keep the "Big Picture" in mind.

Sure, you and another Christian may disagree on a point or two – it may even be a pretty major point. But don't allow that to end your friendship! What's the most important issue in a person's life? Their relationship with God, and their opinion of who Jesus Christ is. If you agree on *that,* everything else should seem pretty minor. Focus on your major areas of agreement, not on your petty disagreements.

> "I am a friend to all who fear You, to all who follow Your precepts."
> —Psalm 119:63

"On the necessary points, unity; on the questionable points, liberty; in everything, love."
–Rupertus Meldenius

4 Cut them some slack.

Why be humble, gentle and patient as the verse to the right admonishes? Because you have faults too, and you hope that others will "make allowance" for yours. You can set the tone in your relationships. If you are harsh and critical of others, they'll probably return the favor. But if your attitude is, "We both need to grow; let's help each other out," your relationship will be deepened, and you will be strengthened. You don't want to condone or facilitate obvious, destructive sin in your brother or sister, but you don't want to jump on every infraction, either.

> "Be humble and gentle. Be patient with each other, making allowance for each other's faults because of your love."
> —Ephesians 4:2 [TLB]

Who in your life needs for you to "cut them some slack"? In what way?

5 When appropriate, confront in love.

Keeping in mind what was written previously about not judging, checking your own eye and making allowances for another's fault, you may encounter an obvious situation where something simply has to be said or done – for the sake of the erring Christian's safety or relationship with God. If you love that person, you will take action. But your action must be founded in love and humility. Your mindset should be, "Look, I'm not saying I'm any better than you are – I'm just one beggar telling another one where the bread is. But here's something that I really feel I need to tell you…"

> "Better is open rebuke than hidden love. The kisses of an enemy may be profuse, but faithful are the wounds of a friend."
> —Proverbs 27:5-6

Extra Insight: Signs of a healthy church:
- Pastor respects and teaches the Bible.
- Prayer and worship are prominent.
- The gospel is clearly presented.
- Focuses on the Great Commission: making disciples of Jesus Christ.
- People are friendly to visitors and each other.
- The ministry is carried on by people besides the pastor and paid staff.
- Generous to those in need.
- Faith in God is factored into all decisions.

6 Examine your motives and tactics.

If you do feel led to speak up about something you observe in another brother or sister, first ask this question of yourself: "Is my objective decapitation or surgery?" When you're finished, will the other person be strengthened by your Spirit-led, loving, humble counsel, or will they be bleeding from multiple stab wounds?

> "There are those who speak rashly like the piercing of a sword, but the tongue of the wise brings healing."
> —Proverbs 12:18

Who is someone you need to pray about confronting in love and humility? On what issue? How will you know if you should go through with it?

Personal Application:

- How many times each week do you normally engage in Christian fellowship (i.e., attend church, a Bible study, a prayer meeting, informal times with other Christians, etc.)?   ⇨ ☐

- Do you feel this is enough for you right now? ❑ Yes ❑ No

- If you plan to change, what changes will you make? How soon?

Scripture Memory Verse:

The Fellowship Connection—
"But encourage one another daily, as long as it is called Today, so that none of you may be hardened by sin's deceitfulness."

—**Hebrews 3:13**

----
[1] Brown, Colin, *Dictionary of New Testament Theology. Vol. 2* (Grand Rapids, MI: Zondervan, 1967), pp. 538ff.

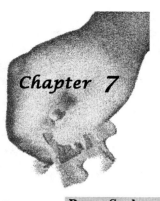

The Bible Connection...
...God's Nourishment For Your Soul

Chapter 7

Why Make This Connection?

1 To find out about God.

What would you do if you wanted to find out all you could about the Queen of England? You could hop on a plane and fly to England, set up a series of meetings and ask her a lot of questions. But not many of us could (a) afford the airfare or (b) gain an audience with her. So you would probably have to settle for reading some books about her. How would you know which books to buy? Some might present an accurate description, but others might have been written by charlatans trying to undermine her by making things up or by publishing false rumors.

First, you had better check the credentials of each author. Find books that were written by people who have studied the Queen thoroughly, or better yet, by someone who actually knew her personally and had spent a lot of time with her. Best of all would be a book that the Queen herself endorsed, saying something like, "This book was written by my good friend, So-and-So, and I agree with everything in it."

Now, what if you wanted to find out all you could about God? Since you can't afford the airfare to visit Him, and very few travel agents would be able to set up a divine audience for you anyway, you'll probably have to resort to literary research again. But again I must ask you, which books will you study?

Here's a suggestion: there is one book which for centuries has been recognized as the source of all books written about God, and that's the Bible. Of course, Muslims, Buddhists, Hindus, and peoples of other religions would disagree with us on that. But if we are coming from a Christian perspective, the Bible is our fount of information. It was written by people who were very close to God. In fact, **2 Timothy 3:16** says that each of its writers wrote things that God Himself specifically directed them to write. Consequently, if you want to find out about God, you should go to the *one book* that claims to be the direct revelation of God to man.

2 To get fed.

You've learned in earlier chapters that you are now a three-dimensional being, composed of a body, a soul and a spirit. We're all well aware of the fact that our physical bodies need to be fed. Most people are regularly reminded of it by hunger pangs. But our souls and our spirits also need nourishment – facts that are not as readily recognized. The Bible is food for your spirit. For example, Jesus said in **Matthew 4:4**, "Man does not live by bread alone, but on every word that comes from the mouth of God." Peter continues the thought in **1 Peter 2:2**, "As newborn babes, desire the pure milk of the word, that you may grow thereby." [NKJV]

A Christian who doesn't get a regular diet of God's Word will end up with an emaciated, weak and sickly spirit. Perhaps you've seen photos of people being liberated from Nazi concentration camps at the end of World War II. If we could take photos of the *spirits* of some Christians, they would probably look very similar to the physical bodies of those pitiable men and women who had been deprived of proper nourishment for so long. Don't let this happen to you! Be sure that you're getting a steady diet of God's meat and potatoes!

Prayer Seed:
"Father, please open my eyes so that I may see wonderful things in Your Bible! Help me gain an appreciation of Your Word as being more important than even my necessary food.[1] Amen."

"I prayed for faith, and thought that some day faith would come down and strike me like lightning. But faith did not seem to come. One day I read in the tenth chapter of Romans, 'Now faith comes by hearing, and hearing by the Word of God.' I had closed my Bible, and prayed for faith. I now opened my Bible, and began to study, and faith has been growing ever since."
–Dwight L. Moody

What IS the Bible?

In its broadest sense, the Bible is a history book. It contains more than *just* history – to be sure. In it you'll find poetry, songs, drama, parables, letters, prophesies, instruction, comedy, tragedy, mystery, love stories, horror, legal treatises, personal correspondence, philosophy, census data, biographies, autobiographies, and more. But taken as a whole, it's a history book. It is a rolling narrative of the times God injected Himself into human history – a record of His encounters with mankind.

People often say, "Oh, if God would only show Himself, then we'd have no trouble believing in Him." Well, that's what the Bible is all about – eyewitness accounts of God showing Himself to man, telling us what He's like, what pleases Him, what displeases Him, where we came from, where we're going, what's good for us, what's bad for us, etc. God has done some pretty awesome things down through the ages, and the Bible is where people have written those things down so that we'll never forget them.

Who Wrote the Bible, and When?

> "Knowing this first, that no prophesy of Scripture is of any private interpretation, for prophesy never came by the will of man, but holy men of God spoke as they were moved by the Holy Spirit."
> —**2 Peter 1:20-21** [NKJV]

According to the verse at the left, what kind of men recorded the prophecies that are contained in Scripture?

Who is the source of the content of the Bible?

> "All Scripture is God-breathed and is useful for teaching, rebuking, correcting and training in righteousness."
> —**2 Timothy 3:16**

What do you think it means in the verse to the left, that "Scripture is God-breathed"?

"Scripture has a double author-ship, and man is only the secondary author; the primary author, through whose initiative, prompting, and enlightenment, and under whose superintendence each human writer did his work, is God the Holy Spirit."

–J. I. Packer[2]

The Human Authors. The Bible is actually 66 books – 39 in the Old Testament and 27 in the New Testament. There were at least forty different authors who contributed to the writing of the Bible – each one directed specifically by the Holy Spirit. These writers came from varied backgrounds, including kings, prophets, philosophers, military men, an heir-apparent turned revolt leader, a farmer, a fisherman, a doctor, a butler, a tax collector, a Jewish Rabbi and others. There are a few of these ancient books whose human authorship has been lost down through the ages. The book of Job is one of these. It is probably the oldest book in the Bible, possibly penned as early as 1850 B.C. Most of the Old Testament books were written between about 1500 B.C. (the five books written by Moses: Genesis, Exodus, Leviticus, Numbers and Deuteronomy) and about 400 B.C. (Malachi). The New Testament books were all written between about 57 A.D. and 96 A.D.

The books of the Bible were written in three different languages. *Hebrew* was the language of the Jews, predominant in the Old Testament. *Greek* was the international language of the day in Christ's time – a lot like English is today – and makes up most of the New Testament. *Aramaic* was a language used sporadically throughout the entire Bible-writing span, but only found in a few books of the Old and New Testaments.

Its writers came from three continents: Asia, Africa and Europe. Some writers were highly educated; others were not. Some wrote with breaking hearts, others from the heights of joy. Some lived in ease and opulence, others experienced great poverty and affliction. Some had walked with God all their lives; others came to Him late in their adult years.

Amazing Unity. Despite the diversity of authors and an expansive time frame, there is a unity of thought, subject matter, perspective, philosophy and purpose that pervades the entire volume unlike any other written work. Imagine building the White House over a period of almost 2000 years with 40 different architects from three continents using three languages. What a mess you'd end up with! But the Bible presents a unified message because of its unique origin – God Himself. As F.F. Bruce wrote, "For all that, the Bible is not simply an anthology; there is a unity which binds the whole together. An anthology is compiled by an anthologist, but no anthologist compiled the Bible."[4]

Structure of the Bible

Open your Bible to its Table of Contents.
You'll immediately notice two major divisions of its 66 books. What are they?

_____

_____

The Old Testament (often abbreviated as "OT") was written in the centuries before Christ came (B.C. = Before Christ) and refers to the old "covenant" or "agreement" that existed between God and man during those days. Central to the Old Testament were the "laws" – rules that God introduced to man which were necessary for a smooth-running society and a pure relationship between God and man. Those who followed the laws would not only experience His blessings here on earth, but would be rewarded with eternal life.

Read **Ezekiel 18:4-9** in the Old Testament of your Bible. This passage describes what "righteous" means in Old Testament terms, and what a "righteous" person can expect: "he…will surely live" (verse 9). Write down five or six behaviors named in this passage that one needed to exhibit without fail if he wanted to inherit this "life."

By the way, there are many, many other passages in the Old Testament that describe many, many other laws that needed to be obeyed. Do you think it would be good enough to obey "most" of these laws "most" of the time, and still make it to heaven? Check **James 2:10** in the New Testament and see if the Bible would agree with that.

❑ It agrees.

❑ It doesn't agree.

❑ I don't know.

If a person did not obey *all* the laws, he would not experience an eternity with God. According to the first verse in the box to the right, what will happen to anyone who sins?

And according to the second and third verses, how many people have sinned?

Would that number include you?

"The soul who sins will die."
—**Ezekiel 18:4b**

"They have all turned aside; together they have become corrupt; there is no one who does good, not even one."
—**Psalm 14:3**

"For all have sinned and fall short of the glory of God."
—**Romans 3:23**

God's Merciful Plan.

Because God knew that no person could live up to His standards for righteousness (which was and is *perfection*), He set up an elaborate system of animal sacrifices that would "cover" a person's sins with the blood of an innocent animal. That may sound horrible to many people, but it underscores the horribleness of sinning against our Creator, and the steep price one has to pay because of his sin. So the Agreement between God and man became very complicated. As man followed the behavioral laws as best he could, and followed the sacrificial laws to cover the penalty when he couldn't, the fellowship between God and man could be maintained. It's interesting to note that even in this Old Covenant the key element that saved a person was *faith* – faith in the one, true God, God's system, and His willingness to forgive.

> "Abram believed the LORD, and He credited it to him as righteousness."
> **—Genesis 15:6**

In the verse to the left, with what does God equate belief or faith?

Note: "Abram" was Abraham's name before God changed it. See **Genesis 17:5**.

But even during the OT times, God knew all along what He was going to do long-term to vastly improve the relationship between Him and man. He was planning to institute a New Covenant, spoken of in **Jeremiah 31:31-34**. Find that passage in your Bible. Notice in verse 33 that it says people won't have to consult books to find out what His laws are. Where does it say God will put His laws?

How do you think the Holy Spirit fits into this plan?

> "The New Testament is enfolded in the Old and the Old Testament is unfolded by the New."
> –Merrill F. Unger[5]

The New Testament

(often abbreviated as "NT") was written after Jesus Christ died and rose again (A.D. = *Anno Domini,* which is Latin for "year of our Lord"). It's called the New Testament because Christ's death on the cross ushered in the New Agreement between God and man. Jesus Christ was the perfect, innocent sacrifice, and while the blood of the animal sacrifices was only capable of *covering* the peoples' sin from God's eyes, Jesus' blood actually took it away – He *paid* for our sins. Under this New Agreement, we are no longer subject to all of those nit-picking laws which we weren't able to obey perfectly anyway. Instead, we have God Himself, in the form of the Holy Spirit, living right inside of us helping us to do right instead of wrong. Consequently, it's our faith in Christ, not how well we can follow all the laws, that makes us righteous in God's eyes.

Read **Romans 8:1-4** in your Bible. Are you "in Christ"? You are if you've received Him into your life. Since you are now "in Christ," what does verse 1 say you will *not* experience from God?

Verse 2 says that you were set free from the "law of sin and death" by something. What was it?

Verse 3 says the Old Testament law was "weak" or "powerless" because of our sinful nature. What does that mean?

Verse 4 says that the righteousness that God requires would be supplied when we do what?

Old Testament Structure

The Old Testament contains a *LOT* more than "rules and regulations," and is, therefore, still very important to us even today. In the Old Testament we can learn a great deal about God's nature and character, what He expects of His people, what He has planned for us in the future, and how to worship Him. We can read the insights and wisdom gained through the centuries by people who walked closely with God.

Look back at your Bible's Table of Contents again. There are several ways the 39 books of the Old Testament could be divided, but here is one popular way. Perhaps you'd like to write these divisions right in your Bible's Table of Contents.

The Historical Books	The Poetical Books	The Prophetical Books
Genesis	Job	Isaiah
Exodus	Psalms	Jeremiah
Leviticus	Proverbs	Lamentations
Numbers	Ecclesiastes	Ezekiel
Deuteronomy	Song of Solomon	Daniel
Joshua		Hosea
Judges		Joel
Ruth		Amos
1 & 2 Samuel		Obadiah
1 & 2 Kings		Jonah
1 & 2 Chronicles		Micah
Ezra		Nahum
Nehemiah		Habakkuk
Esther		Zephaniah
		Haggai
		Zechariah
		Malachi

The Historical Books describe man's history from the time of creation, through the dispersion of mankind around the known world and the Great Flood. Then they narrow their focus to God's dealings with one faithful man: Abraham. These books then trace the growth of his progeny from a small family in southern Babylonia (present-day Iraq), through centuries of slavery in Egypt, their miraculous escape from Egypt under Moses, the conquest of Palestine under Joshua, and eventually to their status as the mightiest nation on earth: Israel under King David. Then we read of Israel's fall over the next few hundred years because its leaders decide to abandon their devotion to God, and follow other so-called gods and their own selfish desires.

The Poetical Books were written primarily during Israel's "Golden Age" and reflect deep wisdom and insight from those who knew God intimately. A large portion of these writings were penned by King David, who was described by God as "a man after My own heart" (**Acts 13:22**), and by David's son Solomon, whom the Bible called "wiser than any other man" (**1 Kings 4:31**).

The Prophetical Books were written during Israel's "Dark Ages," after the kingdom had been split in two during the reign of Solomon's son, Rehoboam. The parts were now called Israel and Judah. Men who walked closely with God spoke and wrote prophecies bringing God's messages to mankind, urging them to return to God for His favor and protection. They also revealed many of God's plans for Israel and for the whole world – things that would occur soon, and things that would occur in the distant future. As the Jews continued to disobey God, the ten tribes of Israel were conquered by the Assyrians and apparently absorbed into the surrounding cultures. The two tribes of Judah were conquered later by the Babylonians and taken as slaves to Babylon. Some of these books were written before this captivity, some during, and some after these two tribes were allowed to return to Palestine about 70 years later.

Don't be embarrassed! What will you say if Obadiah walks up to you in Heaven and asks, "What did you think of my book?"

Jesus in the Histories: (God's promise to Abram regarding his descendant, the Messiah) "I will bless those who bless you, and whoever curses you I will curse; and all the peoples of the earth will be blessed through you."
—**Genesis 12:3**

Jesus in the Poetries: "My God, My God, why have You forsaken Me?"
—**Psalm 22:1**

Jesus in the Prophesies: "For to us a child is born, to us a Son is given, and the government will be on His shoulders. And He will be called Wonderful Counselor, Mighty God, Everlasting Father, Prince of Peace."
—**Isaiah 9:6**
There are many other OT sightings of Jesus!

New Testament Structure

There are several ways one could classify the 27 books of the New Testament, too. The following is one popular way. These books represent a mixture of historical accounts, letters, and an extensive prophecy about the end of the age – each book revealing important facts about Jesus Christ, His eternal kingdom, and the New Agreement under which we now live.

The Historical Books	The Epistles (Letters)		The Apocalypse

Matthew
Mark
Luke
John
Acts
	From Paul to Churches & Groups:
	  Romans
	  1 & 2 Corinthians
	  Galatians
	  Ephesians
	  Philippians
	  Colossians
	  1 & 2 Thessalonians
	  Hebrews
		From Paul to Individuals:
		  1 & 2 Timothy
		  Titus
		  Philemon
		
		From Other Apostles:
		  James
		  1 & 2 Peter
		  1, 2 & 3 John
		  Jude
			Revelation

The Historical Books were written by contemporaries of Jesus and describe His earthly life and what happened in the years following His resurrection. **Matthew** was one of Jesus' twelve disciples, a former tax collector. **Mark**'s book is considered to be virtually a dictation from Peter, because they were close friends for many years. He was also Barnabas's cousin, son of Mary (a very influential disciple in the Church's early days – not Jesus' mother) and a co-worker with Paul in Paul's later years. **Luke** was a physician, Paul's co-worker and Mark's companion. He wrote his account of Christ's life after careful investigation and interviewing numerous eyewitnesses (**Luke 1:1-4**). Luke also researched and wrote the Acts of the Apostles (shortened to "Acts"), a report of the activities of the early church. **John** was also one of Jesus' twelve disciples. He was the one "whom Jesus loved," which describes the closeness of their relationship.

The Epistles were letters written by some of the "pillars" of the early church. The letters held important information that these inspired leaders needed to communicate to the followers of Christ as the Church rapidly spread – kind of like first century e-mail. **Paul** had been a radical Pharisee, which was a sect of the Jews sworn to eliminate Christians and their "heretical doctrines." But he had a personal encounter with the risen Savior and became perhaps His most influential disciple of all time. **Peter** and **John** were two of Jesus' closest disciples, and **James** and **Jude** were Jesus' younger half-brothers, sons of Mary and Joseph.

The Apocalypse, "The Revelation of Saint **John** the Divine" as it's called in some Bibles, or "The Revelation of Jesus Christ" in others, stands in a category by itself. Revelation is a mysterious book full of imagery and difficult passages. There are several opinions regarding what it's about, but it certainly contains many prophetic references that pertain to the end of our present era and the beginning of Christ's reign on earth. These prophecies parallel prophetic passages in Ezekiel, Daniel and many other Old Testament books, as well as much of Jesus' own pronouncements on the subject in **Matthew 24 and 25**. You'll notice that the Apostle John wrote books in all three categories.

Seen on a billboard in the Cleveland area: **"Have you read My #1 bestseller? There will be a test. –God"**

Jesus Christ's Opinion of the Scriptures...

Read **Matthew 22:29, Luke 24:25** and **John 5:39** in your Bible. Write in your own words a summary statement of what Jesus thought about the Bible.

How Do We Know The Bible Is True?

There isn't enough space in this study to go into any great depth on this subject. But here are five key reasons why we can have confidence that the Bible stands alone among all other books as the unique, verifiable, specific Word of God.

Fulfilled Prophecy. Norman Geisler and William Nix: "No unconditional prophecy of the Bible about events to the present day has gone unfulfilled. Hundreds of predictions, some of them given hundreds of years in advance, have been literally fulfilled. [For instance,] the time (**Daniel 9:20-27**), city (**Micah 5:2**), and nature (**Isaiah 7:14**) of Christ's birth were foretold in the Old Testament, as were dozens of other things about His life, death, and resurrection (see **Isaiah 53**)... Other books claim divine inspiration, such as the Koran, the Book of Mormon, and parts of the [Hindu] Veda. But none of those books contains predictive prophecy. As a result, fulfilled prophecy is a strong indication of the unique, divine authority of the Bible."[7]

Textual Reliability. Philosopher and theologian Ravi Zacharias: "In real terms, the New Testament is easily the best attested ancient writing in terms of the sheer number of documents, the time span between the events and the existing documents, and the variety of documents available to sustain or contradict it. There is nothing in ancient manuscript evidence to match such textual availability and integrity."[8]

Archaeological Reliability. Nelson Glueck, former President of the Jewish Theological Seminary in Cincinnati and one of the greatest archaeologists of all time: "It may be stated categorically that no archaeological discovery has ever controverted a single Biblical reference. Scores of archaeological findings have been made which confirm in clear outline or exact detail historical statements in the Bible."[9]

Historical Reliability. Historian John Warwick Montgomery: "To be skeptical of the resultant text of the New Testament books is to allow all of classical antiquity to slip into obscurity, for no documents of the ancient period are as well attested bibliographically as the New Testament."[10]

Scientific Reliability. Nobel Laureate and internationally renowned neuro-biologist Sir John Eccles: "The appearance of conflict between science and religion is a result of ignorance. We come to exist through a divine act... Each of us is a unique, conscious being, a divine creation. It is the religious view. It is the only view consistent with all the evidence."[11]

For Further Insight: *Evidence That Demands A Verdict*[6], a book by noted researcher, author and speaker, Josh McDowell, offers hundreds of pages of objective proof regarding the validity of the Bible and the Christian faith in general. Highly recommended reading! Most of the quotes on this page are taken from collections in that volume.

Benefits Of Reading The Bible

The following passages describe the benefits of studying and applying God's Word to your life. In the box next to each one, write at least one benefit you observe in each passage.

Bible Passage	Benefit(s)
"Do not let this Book of the Law depart from your mouth [i.e., keep talking about it!]; meditate on it day and night, so that you may be careful to do everything written in it. Then you will be prosperous and successful." —**Joshua 1:8**	
"The law of the Lord is perfect, reviving the soul. The statutes of the Lord are trustworthy, making wise the simple. The precepts of the Lord are right, giving joy to the heart. The commands of the Lord are radiant, giving light to the eyes." —**Psalm 19:7-8**	
"The law of his God is in his heart; his feet do not slip." —**Psalm 37:31**	

[Continued next page...]

Bible Passage	Benefit(s)
[Jesus to His disciples] "You are already clean because of the word I have spoken to you." [Jesus praying] "Sanctify them by the truth; Your word is truth." —**John 15:3; 17:17**	
"All Scripture is God-breathed and is useful for teaching, rebuking, correcting and training in righteousness, so that the man of God may be thoroughly equipped for every good work." —**2 Timothy 3:16-17**	
"As newborn babes, desire the pure milk of the word, that you may grow thereby, if indeed you have tasted that the Lord is gracious." —**1 Peter 2:2-3** [NKJV]	

Your Personal Plan

The following illustration shows that there are five ways that a person can get a firm "grasp" on the Word of God. The "Word of God Hand,"[12] created by The Navigators many years ago, demonstrates the importance of getting a balanced input of the different methods of assimilating the Bible into your life. If you try to grasp anything with only one or two fingers, you won't hold it very well. But if you use all five fingers, your grasp will be very strong.

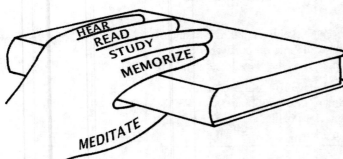

1 Hearing

Read **Luke 6:45-49** in your Bible. In this passage Jesus points out that one must *hear* God's Word, but that's not all. He must hear and... what?

To what does Jesus compare a man who doesn't follow these instructions?

What are some ways that you can be sure to hear the Word of God on a regular basis?

2 Reading

Find and read **Deuteronomy 17:18-20** in your Bible. This was a law which God said all future kings of Israel had to follow. After the king hand-writes his own copy of the law (the first five books of the Bible), for what period of time was he to read it regularly?

What effect was this designed to have on the king?

What effect do you think regular reading of God's Word will have on you?

What can you do to be sure you're reading the Bible on a regular basis?

Note: For a "Read Through The Bible In A Year" schedule, see Appendix #5.

3 Studying

According to the passage on the right, what beneficial objective will you achieve if you spend regular time studying the Bible?

"Study and be eager and do your utmost to present yourself to God approved, a workman who has no cause to be ashamed, correctly analyzing and accurately... handling and skillfully teaching the Word of Truth."
—2 Timothy 2:15
[AMP]

What three things are mentioned that an *unashamed workman* should be able to do with God's Word?

"Studying" the Bible is a more intense and focused activity than simply reading it. As time goes on, you'll be learning many ways to study God's Word so that you can better apply it to your life. Here is a good way to start off. This method is called the **Wow!/Verse/Do/Huh?** approach. Select a chapter of the Bible, read it closely, and then write down four things:

1. **Wow!** – The thing that *amazes* me the most in this chapter:

2. **Verse** – The *verse* I liked most in this chapter: (Write it out – like Israel's kings did!)

3. **Do** – Something I need to *do* in response to reading this chapter:

4. **Huh?** – *Questions* that came to my mind as I read this chapter:

Find **Psalm 1** in your Bible. Employ the **Wow!/Verse/Do/Huh?** method on that chapter.

1. Wow!
2. Verse
3. Do
4. Huh?

"The Bible is the one book which reveals the Creator to the creature He created! No other book that man has conceived can make that statement and support it with fact."
–Billy Graham

Note: Principles for memorizing Scripture can be found in Appendix #2.

4 Memorize

Tests by learning experts have shown that, after a twenty-four hour period, the average person will retain only about 5% of what he hears, about 15% of what he reads, about 35% of what he studies, but 100% of what he memorizes. What does this tell you about the benefits of memorizing key portions of God's Word and "hiding it in your heart"?

> "The law of his God is in his heart; his feet do not slip."
> —**Psalm 37:31**

In the verse to the left the Psalmist connects hiding God's word in your heart with your feet not slipping. What does this mean to you?

5 Meditate

Biblical meditation is "…a private devotional act, consisting in deliberate reflection upon some spiritual truth or mystery, accompanied by mental prayer and by acts of the affection and of the will, especially formation of resolutions as to future conduct." (Unger's Bible Dictionary).

> "Oh, how I love Your law! I meditate on it all day long. Your commands make me wiser than my enemies, for they are ever with me. I have more insight than all my teachers, for I meditate on Your statutes."
> —**Psalm 119:97-99**

Here's another key point of the "Hand" illustration. In the same way that our thumbs can connect with each of our four fingers, so should we meditate on what we hear, read, study and memorize. It's no good to let God's Word flow through you like water through a sieve! As we meditate on it, we capture it, examine it from several different perspectives, think deeply about it, and allow God's Spirit to make it alive in ways that apply specifically to us.

In the passage on the left, how did the Psalmist benefit from meditating on God's Word?

Personal Application:

I will commit to a period of personal Bible study lasting no less than

_____ minutes, _____day(s) a week, for the next

_____weeks, to start on _____ (date). I will ask

_____ to check up on me, give me encouragement, and help me find answers to questions I come up with.

Scripture Memory Verse:

> **The Bible Connection—**
> "All Scripture is God-breathed and is useful for teaching, rebuking, correcting and training in righteousness, so that the man of God may be thoroughly equipped for every good work."
> —**2 Timothy 3:16-17**

WRAP UP:
Jesus asks you, "Will you feed on My Word?"

[1] Thoughts in this prayer are from Psalm 119:18 and Job 23:12.
[2] Comfort, Philip W., Editor, *The Origin of the Bible* (Wheaton: Tyndale House, 1992), p. 31.
[3] Ibid., p. 32.
[4] Bruce, F. F., *The Books and the Parchments: How We Got Our English Bible* (Old Tappan, NJ: Revell, 1950), p. 88.
[5] Unger, Merrill F., *Unger's Bible Dictionary* (Chicago: Moody Press, 1957, 1966), p. 807.
[6] McDowell, Josh D., *The New Evidence That Demands A Verdict* (Nashville: Thomas Nelson Pub., 1999).
[7] Geisler, Norman and Nix, William, *A General Introduction to the Bible* (Chicago: Moody, 1968, 1986), p. 196.
[8] Zacharias, Ravi, *Can Man Live Without God?* (Dallas: Word Publishing, 1994), p. 162.
[9] Glueck, Nelson, *Rivers in the Desert: History of Negev* (New York: Farrar, Straus, and Cadahy, 1959), p. 31.
[10] Montgomery, John W., *History and Christianity* (Downers Grove, IL: InterVarsity Press, 1964), p. 29.
[11] Varghese, Roy Abraham, Ed., *The Intellectuals Speak Out About God* (Dallas: Lewis and Stanley, 1984), p. 50.
[12] Word Hand Illustration, © 1976, The Navigators. Used by permission of NavPress, Colorado Springs, CO. All rights reserved.

The Prayer Connection...
...Communing With The Wisest Being In The Universe

Chapter 8

Why Make This Connection?

Here comes that wonderful person again, Brian thought. *I am so glad she keeps visiting me!*

Brian [fictitious name] is 10 years old and has severe autism. He's a handsome boy, with dark brown hair, blue eyes, and a nice strong chin. And if it weren't that his mind was a prisoner in his malfunctioning brain, he'd be one of the more popular kids at school, just based on looks.

Brian's mother, Monica, helped him up off the floor and led him to his small table in the room that was his world. There she had placed his lunch: a grilled cheese sandwich, one-half an apple cut into four identical slices, three snickerdoodle cookies, and a glass of milk – the same lunch he had every day.

Perfect! She did it again! Just how I like it! Brian felt joy in his heart, though no one on the outside could tell. *She is unbelievably wonderful! Without her, I don't know how I'd survive.*

Monica looked down at him as he began to eat in his mechanical, orderly fashion. "I love you so much, Brian," she told him out loud. "I only wish you knew how much." She reached down and touched the back of his head lovingly.

Brian stiffened. *What was that?* he thought, startled. *I didn't want to feel anything on the back of my head while I was eating. Why did she do that? This is what I don't understand about her. First, she gives me this nice food, and then, she scares me! I wish she would go away!*

"What's wrong, Brian?" Monica asked. "Please tell me, honey. Oh, if only you'd talk to me! How I want to know what's going on inside that head of yours! How I wish we could just… talk. There is so much I want to tell you – and so many things I want to hear you say!"

She knows what I need, and yet, sometimes, it seems like she doesn't care at all. Like earlier today… Brian had gotten so frustrated with the numbness of his body that morning. So, longing to feel *some*thing, he began banging his head against the wall, as those with autism sometimes do. Monica came running and held him in her arms until he quit wanting to bang his head anymore. *Why did she do that? It felt good to me, and she not only made me quit, she MADE me quit! How I hate that!*

Monica knelt down next to Brian and tried to look into his eyes, but Brian would never allow that. He kept staring off to the right, on a spot about a million miles away. "I'll never give up on you, Brian," she said softly. "Even if you never speak, never hug me, never even acknowledge me, I'll always be here for you."

By now, Brian had forgotten the touch on the back of his head. *I wonder why she makes those noises with her mouth. I really do like her. A lot! I wish there was some way that I could let her know… Ah, well. It probably wouldn't mean anything to her anyway. I mean, she's – HER!*

For some Christians, communication with God is about as extensive as Brian's was to his mother. Unlike Monica, God knows our every thought. Yet He still deeply longs to hear us express those thoughts to Him and to find us listening to His thoughts toward us. But so many Christians experience self-imposed *spiritual* autism. Some children with autism recover, but *every* Christian can either avoid or recover from this spiritual condition. It's a matter of choice.

Prayer Seed:
"Father, I am not satisfied just knowing *about* You – I want to *know You!* I want to experience You in the give-and-take of a real relationship. Teach me how to talk with You, to worship You, to treasure, feel at home with, and excel in true Father/child conversation with You. Amen."

"Prayer is a dialogue between two persons who love each other."
–Rosalind Rinker

Ten Facts You Should Know About Prayer

Prayer, at its foundation, is simply talking with God. It can and should be much *more* than that, but in its essence, that describes it pretty well. Though God is far more than a mere person, He is more like a person than anything else our minds can conceive of – which is why we call Him a "personal" God. For this reason, He has asked us to converse with Him as we would with another person.

However, conversing with God isn't *exactly* like conversing with another human being. It's an art, a skill, a learned behavior and a discipline with unique facets about which every Christian needs to be instructed. If the Twelve Apostles, who had been raised as good Jewish boys and been exposed to prayers their entire lives, asked Jesus in **Luke 11:1**, "Lord, teach us to pray," we can assume that people like you and I could also use some education on the subject!

1 You can pray about anything you want to, any time, any place.

Have you ever had any of the following thoughts? (check it if you have)

- ❑ God is certainly too busy to pay attention to *my* needs.
- ❑ My needs aren't significant enough for God's interest.
- ❑ I'm not righteous enough to approach God in prayer regarding my needs.
- ❑ God wouldn't grant my requests because I don't have enough faith.
- ❑ Other negative thoughts you've had? _____

_____

"The prayer of the upright is His delight."
—Proverbs 15:8b

...and by the way, you are one of the "upright," because of what Christ has done for you on the cross!

What does the verse on the left say about God's attitude toward your prayers?

Since God is infinite, everywhere-present, and all-powerful, what does this tell you about His ability to hear and respond to your prayers, while simultaneously hearing and responding to millions of others?

To understand that God *wants* you to talk to Him about anything and everything, look up each of the following verses in your Bible and write down what was prayed for or about, or what we are encouraged to pray for or about in each case.

"True prayer comes not from gritting our teeth, but from falling in love."
–Richard Foster

Bible Passage	Prayer
1 Chronicles 4:10	
Psalm 18:1	
Psalm 22:1-2	
Psalm 143:9	
Matthew 6:11	
Philippians 4:6-7	

2 There are four basic types of prayer: A.C.T.S.

Prayer is meant to be a *lot* more than a "Gimme, gimme" session with God. He *wants* to hear our requests, but He wants more than that. Be sure that your prayer life contains a good balance of these four basic types of prayer – easily remembered by the acrostic **ACTS**.

Adoration — expressing your love to God in worship; praise.

Why do you suppose it's a good idea for husbands and wives to tell each other "I love you"?

How does the "tell-er" benefit from this?

How does the one being told benefit?

Do you realize that you can have a similar effect upon the almighty God of the universe when you tell Him you love Him? It gives Him great pleasure to hear His children express their love to Him; it "blesses" Him! Wouldn't it be cruel to withhold this blessing from God after all He's done for us? Tell Him you love Him often – not because He demands it or needs to be reminded, but because it ministers to Him! It's the normal response of a grateful and loving heart!

Confession — agreeing with God about your sin.

Read **Psalm 66:18** in your Bible. What effect does unconfessed sin have on your prayers?

Read **1 John 1:9** in your Bible. What effect does confessional prayer have on your sin?

The Greek word for "confession" in the New Testament is *homologeo*, which literally means "to say the same thing," i.e., to agree with God when He points out sin in our lives. We don't have to then perform some mighty act to cleanse ourselves from our sin; He tells us to simply agree with Him about it being wrong, and He'll take care of it. He's not asking us to do a massive search in every nook and cranny of our lives to be sure we are totally sin-free. That would take a *long* time! He'll select specific issues that He wants us to deal with, then point them out to us.

Thanksgiving — thanking God for things He's done.

The verse on the right is from a passage that describes why God gives unrighteous people over to their own preferences for perversion and sinfulness (**Romans 1:18-32**). They have an innate knowledge of God, but their thoughts become futile, and their hearts become darkened because they don't glorify God as God *and* because of what else?

Therefore, when we omit thanksgiving from our communications with God, would you say we were drawing more from the well of our Old Nature, or from the well of our New Nature?

❑ New Nature

❑ Old Nature

Note: The "Old Well/ New Well" illustration can be found in Chapter 4.

Insight: disobey your Old Nature and give thanks to God frequently!

> "One day, when all the secrets of God are fully understood by the children of men, most Christians will marvel that they never fully appropriated the mighty spiritual resources of God's promises to all who believe in Christ, because they never had learned how to pray."[2]
> –Bill Bright

> "I will bless the Lord at all times; His praise shall continually be in my mouth."
> —Psalm 34:1 [NKJV]

> "Because, although they knew God, they did not glorify Him as God, nor were thankful, but became futile in their thoughts, and their foolish hearts were darkened."
> —Romans 1:21

*S*upplication — *making requests of God.*

God wants you to know that not only *can* you bring your requests to Him, He *wants* you to! It's a privilege He's extended to you as one of His children! He knows it makes you happy, and He *loves* to make you happy! What does the verse on the left say is one of the reasons why God likes to hear and grant our requests?

3 *God really does listen to your prayers.*

Praying is not merely some psychological exercise or discipline. It's not like a form of meditation where we engage in it strictly for our own benefit and edification. It's a genuine conversation. You speak, and God listens. He'll speak back to you through the Bible, or through circumstances, or even through direct impressions to your mind.

Read **Psalm 94:9** in your Bible. What main point is this verse making?

"I waited patiently for the Lord; He turned to me and heard my cry."
—**Psalm 40:1**

"The eyes of the Lord are on the righteous, and His ears are attentive to their cry … The righteous cry out, and the Lord hears them; He delivers them from all their troubles."
—**Psalm 34:15,17**

"You hear, O Lord, the desire of the afflicted; You encourage them, and You listen to their cry."
—**Psalm 10:17**

Identify the common theme in each of the three scripture passages above.

4 *Faith is vital in prayer.*

Let's say I asked you to do me a favor. Then, at the end of my request, I suddenly changed my tone and said, "But I don't know why I'm asking you, anyway. You'll probably say no. Never mind!" Do you think you'd eagerly and graciously set out to fulfill my request? Not likely.

Many Christians come to God with the same attitude – no confidence in God's willingness or ability to answer their prayers. Is it any wonder why God remains unresponsive to their requests? Throughout the Bible, God says, "If you want Me to work in and through you, you must have faith that I can and will do it." Faith is one of the primary characteristics that God wants to develop in you, so He'll respond to your faith in amazing ways!

In the verse to the left, why do you think God requires that those who would approach Him must believe that He exists and cares?

Read **Matthew 13:54-58.** Why was Jesus' miraculous ministry severely hampered in His own home region?

5 God answers prayer in four ways.

Just asking God for something in prayer doesn't automatically guarantee that we will receive it. God is all-wise. He knows that some of the things we desire would be good for us, others would harm us, others would be good at a later time, and still others would be good if certain conditions are met. That's why He will answer every prayer we pray by saying either **Yes**, **No**, **Wait** or **If**. As His children, our attitude toward His decision regarding our prayers should be one of quiet acceptance – because we have confidence in His vast wisdom.

If my toddler asked me to let her play with the nice, shiny butcher knife, I'd be a terrible father if I let her. She might not understand my decision – even if I tried real hard to explain it to her. Sshe might cry and throw a temper tantrum, trying to convince me to change my mind. But I would remain firm in my negative resolve, because I love her. Eventually, I *will* let her use the butcher knife, but not until she's older and better able to handle it.

Examples of Yes, No, Wait, If. Look up each of the passages in the left column and write a brief summary of each verse in the middle column. In the right column, note which of the four responses God gave to each request: Yes, No, Wait or If. (There will be two passages for each type of response.)

> "Prayer-faith is an absolute confidence applied to the *Receiver* of the request: God. It's not just confidence as to whether or not God is able to remove the mountain but also a confidence that God *knows* if it is really best for the mountain to be removed and in what direction."[3]
> –Curtis C. Mitchell

Bible Passage	Passage Summary — Request & Answer	God's Response
1 Samuel 1:11,19-20		
Matthew 26:36-45		
Genesis 15:2-6; 21:1-7	Abram's desire: God's answer 15 years later:	
[Solomon's prayer at the dedication of the temple.] **2 Chronicles 6:36-39 and 7:14**	Solomon's request: God's conditional answer:	
2 Kings 6:15-20		
2 Corinthians 12:7-10		
Exodus 2:23-25 and Psalm 105:26-38	The desire of the Israelite slaves: God's answer *after* the Plagues: (Psalm 105:37)	
Numbers 21:4-9	God would heal them on what condition?	

Hypothetical thought: Consider God's position as the great "Prayer Answerer." Here's a supplication someone makes to Him: "Lord, we simply cannot make ends meet around here! With the new baby, and the rent, and the car payments, we really need more income. Could You please let me get that new position at work with the increased salary?" Write down one hypothetical reason why God might answer with a "No," and one reason for a "Wait" answer.

NO. _____

WAIT. _____

> **"Delight yourself in the Lord and He will give you the desires of your heart."**
> **—Psalm 37:4**

When He is our delight, our focus, our top priority, our desires will perfectly align themselves with His desires and His will.

6 "Yes" answers require certain conditions.

An important principle in the science of interpreting the Bible is that you must not construct a doctrine from just one verse. You need to consider all that the Bible has to say on the subject. Otherwise you'll be like the three blind men trying to describe an elephant after only examining a small part of it. One man felt its broad side and said it was big and flat, like a house. One felt its trunk and said it was like a snake. One felt its leg and said it was like a tree. It's the same with understanding how to get "Yes" answers to our prayers. We need to consider *all* the conditions the Bible presents.

Below are ten Bible passages, each mentioning a requirement that must be present if we are to get an affirmative answer to our prayers. Write the requirement in the column on the right.

Bible Passage	Condition for "Yes" Answers
"…I tell you the truth, if you have faith as small as a mustard seed, you can say to this mountain, 'Move from here to there' and it will move. Nothing will be impossible for you." **—Matthew 17:20b**	
"Therefore I tell you, whatever you ask for in prayer, believe that you have received it, and it will be yours." **—Mark 11:24**	[Key phrase and tense: "believe that you HAVE received it"]
"When you stand praying, if you hold anything against anyone, forgive him, so that your Father in heaven may forgive you your sins." **—Mark 11:25**	
Read **Luke 18:1-8** in your own Bible.	
Read **Luke 18:9-14** in your own Bible.	
"I will do whatever you ask in My name, so that the Son may bring glory to the Father." **—John 14:13**	[2 conditions in this verse]
"If you remain in Me and My words remain in you, ask whatever you wish, and it will be given you." **—John 15:7**	
"You do not have because you do not ask God." **—James 4:2b**	
"When you ask, you do not receive, because you ask with wrong motives, that you may spend what you get on your pleasures." **—James 4:3**	
"This is the assurance we have in approaching God: that if we ask anything according to His will, He hears us. And if we know that He hears us- whatever we ask – we know that we have what we asked of Him." **—1 John 5:14-15**	

"Prayer is an extremely difficult discipline because it demands putting my kneecaps where my mouth is."[4] –Fred Askins

7 There is great authority as you pray "in Jesus' name."

You may have heard people who pray in public end their prayers with "in Jesus' name, amen." There's nothing wrong with this, but to pray "in Jesus' name" is a lot more than just tacking that phrase on the end of your prayers and expecting God's subsequent rubber stamp.

What does it mean to pray "in Jesus' name"? It means to lay your requests before God the Father as an official representative of Jesus Christ and, therefore, in Christ's perfect standing before God. It's like when the policeman pounds on the door and says, "Open up in the name of the law!" He's not expecting anyone to open the door just because *he's* asking; he expects it to be opened because he is there representing the full authority of the law.

All through the centuries, followers of God were allowed to approach His throne of grace and make requests of Him. Often their prayers were not honored because they themselves had a less-than-honorable standing before God. But then an amazing thing happened: God the Son showed up on earth in human form! Now a select few could get their needs met by bringing them to Jesus Christ, who *always* had an immediate entrance to the Father. This is terrific for the few, but what about the rest of the world? In the passage on the right, Jesus tells His followers that after He rises from the dead, they won't need to use Him as an intermediary any more, because they can take their supplications directly to the Father. They would no longer be going on their own merit – they could go on *His*. He gave us His authority and perfect standing with God so that when we come before the Father with our requests, He doesn't see a flawed and sinful man. He sees *His Son*, whose requests He is delighted to hear!

But what do you think? If I showed up in God's heavenly courts drunk, dirty, my heart full of lies and lust, and I said, "I come before you today in the name of Your Son, Jesus Christ, as His representative," how do you think the Father would respond to me?

God the Father knows our heart. And though neither He nor we could ever expect us to achieve sinless perfection before approaching Him, He knows whether we are at least trying to respond to the corrective promptings of the Holy Spirit. What do you think would be a few of the characteristics of someone who was praying "in Jesus' name"?

8 Persistence is a true "yes-answer-enhancer."

One might think that it would show more logic, humility, and greater faith to bring our petitions before the Father *once* and then wait patiently for His response – not mentioning them again. But it's interesting to note what the Son of God has to say on this matter – and He's someone who should know!

You've already read **Luke 18:1-8** in section #6 on *"'Yes' answers require certain conditions,"* which addresses persistence in prayer. Now find **Luke 11:5-13** in your Bible and read it.

In **verses 9 & 10**, the Greek that Jesus used was in the "linear tense," and could be best interpreted, "ask and keep on asking… seek and keep on seeking… knock and keep on knocking…" What do you think He's trying to tell us regarding persistency in our prayers?

Why do you think God might want us to keep on asking, seeking and knocking?

> "Satan laughs at our toiling, mocks at our wisdom, but trembles when he sees even the weakest saint on his knees."
> –Unknown

> "In that day [after My resurrection] you will no longer ask Me anything. I tell you the truth, My Father will give you whatever you ask in My name. Until now you have not asked for anything in My name. Ask and you will receive, and your joy will be complete."
> —John 16:23-24

> "Behind every work of God, you will always find some kneeling form."
> –Dwight L. Moody

9 Tolerated sins hamper our "Yes" answers.

> "If I had cherished sin in my heart, the Lord would not have listened."
> —**Psalm 66:18**

> "But your iniquities have separated you from you God; your sins have hidden His face from you so that He will not hear."
> —**Isaiah 59:2**

> "He who conceals his sins does not prosper, but whoever confesses and renounces them finds mercy."
> —**Proverbs 28:13**

According to the three verses above, what effect does known, unrepented-of sin have on our lines of communication with God?

"In all of us, God 'still' holds only a part. D-Day is only a week ago. The bite so far taken out of Normandy shows small on the map of Europe. The resistance is strong, the casualties heavy, and the event uncertain. There is, we have to admit, a line of demarcation between God's part in us and the enemy's region. But it is, we hope a fighting line; not a border fixed by agreement."[5]
—**C.S. Lewis**

Why God Won't Ignore Your Sin

Dennis came to Mike to ask if he could borrow his pick-up truck to help a friend move. But as they were talking, Mike noticed a red stain on Dennis' sleeve. Blood!

"Dennis, did you know you're bleeding?"

"Yeah, no big deal. It'll probably stop. Now, about your truck. Can I have it? I'll bring it back with a full gas tank."

The bloodstain grew rapidly, and then began to drip on the floor.

"Uh, I really think we need to get you to a doctor, Dennis. You must have cut an artery somehow!"

Dennis is getting perturbed. "Would you forget about the blood, Mike? I'm talking to you about your *truck*! Don't you care about anything I say? Are you going to keep changing the subject, or go get your keys?"

Mike responds, equally perturbed. "I'm not going to say another word about my truck until *after* we get you to the hospital and get that cut sewn up – or else you won't be alive to use my truck at all!"

❉   ❉   ❉

Dennis had noble intentions – to help his friend move. But Mike noticed a much more urgent need in Dennis' life. We, too, come to God with many noble requests, but He's not going to pay attention to *them* if He sees sin in our life, cutting us to ribbons.

---

10 Don't forget to listen.

You already know a very important point about prayer – assuming you know anything at all about conversation. If, as Rosalind Rinker said, "Prayer is a dialog between two persons who love each other," it's a good idea to spend *some* of the time listening to what God might want to say.

You can sit quietly, perhaps with an open Bible in front on you, perhaps meditating on a Bible verse, and wait expectantly on the Lord. Take the initiative and ask God if there is anything in particular He would like to say to you. Then wait and listen.

> "Be still, and know that I am God..."
> —**Psalm 46:10a**

> "I have stilled and quieted my soul; like a weaned child with its mother..."
> —**Psalm 131:2a**

In the two verses on the left, what do you think it means to "be still" or to "still and quiet" your soul?

In **1 Samuel 3:10**, Samuel said to God, "Speak, for Your servant is listening." Yet too often our prayers are, "Listen, for Your servant is speaking!" Find **Isaiah 55:2b, 3** in your Bible, and write down what God would like for us to do.

"Prayer is first of all listening to God. It's openness. God is always speaking; He's always doing something. Prayer is to enter into that activity."
                                    –Henri Nouwen

"Prayer starts with God. Our desire to pray is the result of His call to prayer. He has something to say. Our responsibility is to listen to what He wants to give us for our problems and potential."
                                    –Lloyd Ogilvie

"Spiritual battles are won by following revelation given by the Holy Spirit. If we listen to God with child-like dependency, He will guide us to victory."
                                    –John Dawson

Who Should I Pray For?

Here's a "handy" illustration to guide you in your prayer times. Just look at your hand to remember for whom you should be praying![6]

Your **Pointer** reminds you of those who teach, including pastors, missionaries and teachers. They need support and wisdom in pointing others in the right direction.

Your **Middle Finger** is the tallest, reminding you to pray for our leaders: the President and other political leaders, business leaders, school administrators, your boss, etc. They shape our cities, states and nation, and need God's guidance.

Your **Ring Finger** is your weakest finger, reminding you to pray for those who are weak, in trouble or in pain. They need your prayers day and night.

Your **Thumb** is nearest to you, so begin your prayers by praying for those closest to you: your spouse, children, parents, siblings, other relatives, friends, and neighbors.

Your **Pinky** is your smallest finger, reminding you to place yourself last in relation to God and others. Pray about your needs, joys, frustrations, plans and dreams.

Prayer Diary

Here's a suggestion that will make you more pro-active in your prayer life, and greatly increase your faith. Make a number of sheets of paper that have three columns. Title them "Date," "Request" and "Answer." Each time you feel led to begin praying for a particular request, write it down and date it. Then, when God provides an answer (any one of the four types), write a summary of it in the third column. As you look back over your diary, you'll be amazed at how God has responded to your prayers! *[Two printed forms that you may copy and use are included in Appendix #5.]*

Prayer Project:

I will begin praying for these three requests immediately (personal or for others). I will commit to praying for them until God gives me a definite answer. **I will be persistent!**

1.

2.

3.

Personal Application:

I will commit to a period of personal prayer lasting no less than _____ minutes,

_____day(s) a week, for the next _____weeks, to start on _____ (date). I will ask

_____ to check up on me, give me encouragement, and help me find

answers to questions I think of with regarding my prayer life.

Scripture Memory Verse:

WRAP UP:
Jesus asks you, "Will you come talk with Me?"

> **The Prayer Connection—**
> "Until now you have not asked for anything in My name. Ask and you will receive, and your joy will be complete."
> —**John 16:24**

[1] Duewel, Wesley L., *Touch The World Through Prayer* (Grand Rapids, MI: Zondervan, 1986), p. 21.
[2] Bright, Bill, *Learn How You Can Help Change the World Thru Prayer* (San Bernardino, CA: CCC, 1975), p. 1.
[3] Mitchell, Curtis C., *Praying Jesus' Way* (Old Tappan, NJ: Revell, 1977), p. 99-100.
[4] Askins, Fred, "Prayer: The Great Rusty Cannon," *Discipleship Journal,* Issue 49 (1989), p. 15.
[5] Lewis, C.S., *Prayer: Letters to Malcolm* (Glasgow, Scotland: William Collins Sons, 1963), p. 34.
[6] Original art work done by none other than Big Al Langness.

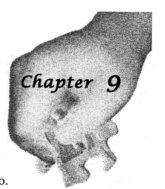

The Witnessing Connection...
...Spreading God's Connections Around

Chapter 9

Why Make This Connection?

One of history's most enigmatic figures was Luigi Tarisio. Born in Milan, Italy, in 1792, he was an apprentice carpenter by trade. Throughout his life, Tarisio scoured the countryside looking for rare violins. He had a knack for hunting down the rarest of violins made by master craftsmen. After purchasing them, he tucked them safely away in his tiny apartment, out of harm's way. Except for a few instruments that he sold through the years to make ends meet, most of the violins he bought were kept hidden in his home. Some of the world's finest musicians would visit Tarisio just to see them. He would let them look at his precious treasures, but he would never allow them to be played.

His rarest violin was a masterwork created by Antonio Stradivari. Tarisio had bragged of its beauty, but he wouldn't bring it out into the open. Ever. He called it "The Messiah," because as he put it, "It's like the Messiah whom we all wait for but never see."

Tarisio died in October of 1854. In his disheveled apartment were 246 exquisite violins, including The Messiah. In his devotion to violins, he had robbed the world for years of all the beautiful music the instruments could have brought had they not been locked away.[1]

God does not want us to keep His *true* Messiah locked up inside – precious to us, but hidden from the world. We have been so incredibly blessed by His presence in our lives – and His desire is to bless others also. How could we even *think* about selfishly hoarding Him in the inaccessible apartments of our lives?

As Bill Bright, founder of Campus Crusade for Christ often asks, "What is the greatest thing that ever happened to you?" Most of us would answer, "Coming to know Jesus Christ as my Savior," because the ramifications of that experience are eternal. His next question is always, "Then, what is the greatest thing you can do for another person?" How would you answer him?

What are your current thoughts and feelings on this subject of sharing your faith in Christ with others? Does the idea excite you or strike fear in your heart? Do you feel bold about it, or do you fear the rejection that sometimes comes? Do you feel confident about it, or confused? Is it an "ought to/got to" or a "want to"?

Prayer Seed:
"Thank you, Father, for desiring so strongly to use someone like me in Your re-conquest of Planet Earth. Please give me the love, the skills, the knowledge, and the supernatural connections to be an effective instrument of Your love in this pursuit. Amen."

"One of the greatest misconceptions of the centuries, in my opinion, is the idea so prevalent among Christians that men do not want God. Wherever I go – in this country or in other countries – I find ample proof that just the opposite is true. The Holy Spirit has created a hunger for God in the hearts of multitudes."[2]
–Bill Bright

What Is The Gospel?

Here are three scriptural "nutshells" of the Gospel. Find each one in your Bible and write down the key elements of the gospel mentioned in each one.

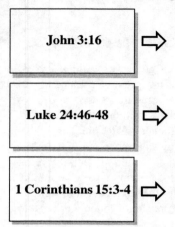

A Summary of The Gospel: All men are guilty of sin before God. The penalty for sin is death – eternal separation from God. But because of His great love for us, God sent His Son, Jesus Christ, to take the penalty of our sin on Himself when He died on the cross. Three days later He was resurrected from the dead and is alive today and forever. If a person will repent (that is, change his mind and go back in God's direction) of his sinful way of life, and have faith that Jesus Christ is the Son of God and able to save him from eternal death, he will be forgiven, placed in right standing with God, and gain eternal life.

Were there any elements of the above definition that you didn't understand when you received Christ? If so, which ones – and do you understand them now?

What Is Witnessing?

In its broadest sense, witnessing is simply telling what you know. As Peter and John said to the Jewish authorities (who were trying to make them stop witnessing), "We cannot stop speaking what we have seen and heard" (**Acts 4:20**). What have you seen and heard about Jesus? As you relate those things to others who don't know Him yet, you are witnessing.

Think about a courtroom scene. Each person there has a specific assignment and responsibility. As the "witness," what would your responsibilities include?

Would it be your job to *convince* the jury of anything? That may happen, but it's not your assignment. Do you have to act as the prosecutor in the case? The defense attorney? The judge? No, all you need to do is "tell what you've seen and heard," and God will do the rest.

A witness in a court of law is supposed to "tell the truth, the whole truth, and nothing but the truth." As a witness for Christ, it would be dishonest to misrepresent yourself by exaggerating or minimizing what has taken place in your life. To hold back the truth wouldn't do either. Simply be honest and prepared to let your life be an open book to be read by anyone interested. If you can do this, you will be a truly useful and effective witness for Christ!

"Let the redeemed of the Lord say so, whom He has redeemed from the hand of the enemy!"
—**Psalm 107:2** [NASB]

God's Role In Witnessing

As you're busy telling someone "what you've seen and heard," God is also busy – probably in ways that neither you nor the person you're talking to are aware of.

Read **John 16:7-11** in your Bible. [The "Helper" or the "Comforter" spoken of in this passage is the Holy Spirit, whom God would send soon after Christ's resurrection.] What does it say the Holy Spirit will do?

According to the verse on the right, would you say that the gospel message is just like any other kind of message, or does it have a more unique facet to it? What is it?

"As the rain and the snow come down from heaven, and do not return to it without watering the earth and making it bud and flourish, so that it yields seed for the sower and bread for the eater, so is My word that goes out from My mouth: it will not return to Me empty, but accomplish what I desire and achieve the purpose for which I sent it."
—Isaiah 55:10-11

According to the verse on the left, what promise do we have when we share God's word through the gospel message?

So, what can you conclude about what God will be doing as you are sharing the gospel with someone?

Since God's role in a fruitful witnessing experience is crucial, what part do you think *prayer* should play in your witnessing strategy?

Why Should I Witness?

Below are several passages that will help answer that question. Look up the verse in the left column and record your observations in the right one.

Passage	I should witness because…
Mark 16:15	
Luke 19:10 & 2 Peter 3:9	
Romans 10:13-14	
John 10:10b	
Luke 9:26	

How Do I Witness?

Witnessing involves two very important facets. We witness through the kind of **life** we live, and we witness by our **words** – verbal communication. One without the other is less than optimal. Our lives communicate to non-Christians the *context* and verification of the message we share, while the words communicate the *content* – the issues that need to be understood in order to make a decision regarding Christ. Living the life without sharing the words leaves the unbeliever *foggy* about what he's supposed to do. Sharing the words but living a life that contradicts our message leaves the unbeliever *certain*... certain he isn't interested in the hollow words we're speaking!

Witnessing through our lives

Given a choice, most people will opt for what they *see* over what they *hear*. If you were walking in a rough neighborhood one night and saw a dangerous-looking man standing at the entrance of an alley, holding a half-consumed whiskey bottle and a baseball bat, what would you think? But would it change your opinion if you then heard him say, "Pardon me, would you mind coming over here a minute? I seem to have lost my contact lens..."? Sounds pleasant enough, but what you're *looking* at is quite *un*pleasant, and you'd go nowhere near him.

Likewise, those who don't know Christ will observe our lives, and they will always assume that our *actions* portray the truth about us and how genuine our message is. Talk is cheap.

In the verse on the left, what are we directed to do?

What are some ways you could do this in your particular life context?

This verse says our actions should have a two-phase objective. What are the two phases?

When we forget the fact that our actions form a large part of our Christian witness, we hurt the advance of the Kingdom of God. Read **1 Corinthians 15:34.** In this verse, Paul blasted the Corinthian Christians because they were apparently unconcerned about the negative effect their sinning was having on the non-Christians around them. What do you think he would say to the modern Christian church today?

Witnessing through our words

It's very good when non-Christians can see God shining through us in our actions. Those whose hearts God has prepared will be drawn to that light. If nothing else, they'll be curious about what makes us tick. So when they are standing there ready to listen, what do we say?

There are four key facts which – if they are properly communicated and understood – will help a person understand the gospel and be able to make a decision to receive Christ. A fuller development of these four facts can be found in Appendix #1 of this book (pages 143-147).

1 **God loves every individual and created us to have eternal fellowship with Him.**

According to the verse on the left, what was God's primary motivation for sending His Son to die for the sins of mankind?

[Concerning Bible covers] "Men may not read the gospel in sealskin, or the gospel in morocco, or the gospel in cloth covers; but they can't get away from the gospel in shoe leather."
–Donald Grey Barnhouse

"Let your light shine before men, that they may see your good deeds and praise your Father in heaven."
—Matthew 5:16

"If Christians would consistently live according to the teachings of Christ as found in the Bible, all of India would be Christian today."
–Mohandas K. Gandhi

"For God so loved the world that He gave His one and only Son, that whoever believes in Him shall not perish but have eternal life."
—John 3:16

2 **Every individual has sinned, severing this fellowship with God, ultimately resulting in eternal separation if not resolved.**

According to the two verses on the right, how many people have sinned? _____

How many people need the salvation that God offers through Christ? _____

What if someone you're witnessing to disagrees with this fact, and feels that he has not sinned, nor that he is in need of a Savior?

> "We all, like sheep, have gone astray, each of us has turned to his own way; and the Lord has laid on Him [Jesus] the iniquity of us all."
> —**Isaiah 53:6**

> "For all have sinned and fall short of the glory of God."
> —**Romans 3:23**

3 **God sent His Son, Jesus Christ, to take the penalty of our sin on Himself, making reunion with God possible.**

In **1 Peter 3:18** (on the right), what was God's objective in sending Christ to die?

After Jesus died, He was made alive again by the Holy Spirit. What did His resurrection prove to those who had been following Him — to those He had told He was the Son of God?

> "For Christ died for sins once for all, the righteous for the unrighteous, to bring you to God. He was put to death in the body but made alive by the Spirit."
> —**1 Peter 3:18**

4 **The sacrifice of Jesus Christ is applied to us individually as we, by an act of our will, receive Christ through faith.**

Is it enough simply to *know* the three preceding facts, or does **John 1:12** (on the right) indicate that we need to take some sort of action? If so, what action is necessary?

Could someone be a Christian by virtue of the fact that he was born into a Christian family? Could someone accidentally or passively become a Christian? Why or why not?

> "Yet to all who received Him, to those who believed in His name, He gave the right to become children of God."
> —**John 1:12**

A Great Tool For Witnessing: These same four facts can be found in almost every witnessing approach. But a very effective presentation of them is available in a tract written by Bill Bright titled "Have You Heard of the Four Spiritual Laws?" (now also available under the title "Would You Like To Know God Personally?"). Over the years, *millions* of people have come to a saving knowledge of Christ through reading this tract or studying it with a Christian. You can order it in packs of 50 through New Life Resources at (800) 827-2788 or on their web site: www.campuscrusade.org.

Witnessing and the Word: Use it!

Read **Hebrews 4:12** in your Bible. What do you think it means when it says God's Word is "living and active"?

How would this be helpful in a witnessing situation?

Extra Insight: Whenever you can, use the Bible while witnessing. For example, share verses you've memorized or open the Bible and have him/her read key passages out loud. Three of the most powerful words in Billy Graham's evangelistic talks are, "The Bible says..."

Your Testimony

When it comes to the gospel, people can always disagree with your logic, your theology, your assumptions and your conclusions. But one thing they can't dispute is *your experience*.

In **John 9**, Jesus gave sight to a man who had been blind since birth. Jesus' enemies questioned the man's healing and tried to get him to deny that it was a miracle. They told the man that Jesus was a sinner. They badgered him, cross-examined him and hurled insults at him. He didn't have all the answers – not by a long shot! But the main point he shared that they couldn't dismantle was: "One thing I do know, that whereas I was blind, now I see!" (verse 25).

While it is a good idea to know how to share a Scripture-based gospel presentation, one of the best ways to "prepare the soil" is to share your own personal testimony – a well-thought-out capsulization of how you came to know Christ which can be shared in two to three minutes.

A personal testimony usually is composed of three parts:

　　1. Before - What your life was like before receiving Christ.

　　2. How – Exactly how you came to the decision of receiving Christ.

　　3. After – What your life was like after receiving Christ.

It's best if you can also weave the gospel message through your testimony, so that by the time you're finished, the listener knows of his need for Christ and how to become a Christian.

Read **Acts 26:1-23** in your Bible. Paul had been captured and imprisoned by the Jews and was appearing before King Agrippa. To Paul, this seemed like an excellent time to share his testimony! Write a summary of Paul's testimony in the four spaces below:

Paul's life **Before**: Verses 1-11	**How** Paul was saved: Verses 12-18	Paul's life **After**: Verses 19-23	Verses that contain elements of the gospel

ASSIGNMENT: On a separate sheet(s) of paper, write out the three parts of your testimony – one-third to one-half page for each part. If you became a Christian at a young age and can't remember your conversion, then focus on a major crisis and turning point in your life, where you finally let Jesus Christ become your Lord (assuming you *have* made Him Lord; if not, today's the day!).

As you write, here are a few things to avoid:

1. Exaggeration ("I used to get drunk daily at age four.")

2. Glittering generalities ("My life was *horrible* before I met Christ. And now everything is absolutely wonderful!")

3. Talking negatively about any particular person, church or denomination.

4. Religious lingo ("I was convicted by the Holy Ghost, then repented and was saved!")

5. Too much detail; too many points; irrelevant points.

6. Focusing on and sensationalizing your sinful pre-Christian era. (Instead, focus on how the Holy Sprit has worked in your life. Give Jesus center-stage, not Satan!)

Cool Web Site:
"Five Clicks To Sharing Your Faith." This site will help you compose your testimony in an interactive, entertaining and creative way. Go to **www.5clicks.com** for excellent insight on this subject.

What If They Reject Me?

Obviously, some people won't like hearing the gospel. In the verse on the right, who did Jesus say is actually being rejected when someone doesn't respond positively to your evangelistic overtures?

Always remember that they are not rejecting you as a person. In their minds, they are merely disagreeing with an opinion you hold. They do that all the time in a variety of contexts – and so do you. The only ones they are really rejecting are Jesus Christ and His Holy Spirit – who are trying to convince them of their need for a Savior. So try not to take it personally.

Another important point to remember is this: **witnessing is not always followed by a conversion event**. No 1-to-1 ratio here! Witnessing is a **process** that can eventually lead to an **event**. Most non-Christians (especially adults) need to go through a process of supernatural education that will gradually dispel their doubts and dissipate the smoke-screens Satan has been setting up for years. A person may hear the Good News from five or ten different sources, moving a little closer to faith in Christ each time, until finally, he's ready to "take the plunge." Each time you share the gospel with someone, you're helping move that person a little closer to the Lord.

Read **1 Corinthians 3:5-10** in your Bible. Do you see the existing partnership among the witnessers (Apollos was another evangelist like Paul)? What do you think it means in verse 6 where it says, "I planted the seed, Apollos watered…"

What point was Paul making when he concluded that verse with "…but God made it grow."?

> "He who listens to you listens to Me; he who rejects you rejects Me; but he who rejects Me rejects Him who sent Me."
> —Luke 10:16

I Can't Answer Their Questions!

You're not alone! People can ask millions of questions about Christianity. Sometimes they are legitimate roadblocks to their faith; other times they are simply smoke-screens that they set off so they won't have to deal with the *true* issue concerning accepting or rejecting Jesus Christ as their Savior. Trust the Holy Spirit to give you insight as to which it is.

However, if a question comes up as you are sharing the gospel that might take the conversation down a "rabbit trail," you might want to say something like, "That's a good question, and it deserves an answer. But for now, could we carry on through this presentation? If it's not answered by the time we get to the end, ask it again."

If you are asked what you feel is a legitimate question and you don't know the answer, simply say, "I don't know the answer to that, but I'll find out for you." Then go find out! Be like Dawson Trotman, founder of The Navigators, who made it a personal policy never to be stumped by the same question twice!

What advice does Paul give to Timothy, his young disciple, in **2 Timothy 2:16, 23-26**?

In the verse on the right, we are admonished to be pro-active in our preparations to answer people's questions. What practical steps can you take to obey this admonition?

> Asked incredulously, upon discovering his friend didn't have any gospel tracts with him: "Don't you carry anything to give to people who need the Lord? What good is a soldier without any ammunition?"[4]
> –Dawson Trotman

> "Always be ready to give a logical defense to any one who asks you to account for the hope that is in you, but do it courteously and respectfully."
> —1 Peter 3:15b [AMP]

How Can I Begin A Witnessing Conversation?

Questions are always a good way to draw people out. Read **Acts 8:26-38** in your Bible. How did Philip begin his witnessing encounter with the Ethiopian?

Here are some ideas of how you might start a conversation about Christ:

- Do you ever think about spiritual things (or God, heaven, the supernatural, life after death)?
- What's your spiritual background?
- Do you go to church? Why or why not? What do they teach you at your church?
- Would you say you were satisfied with your relationship with God, or do you feel like it's lacking something?
- Do you have a relationship with God, or are you still "on the way"?
- I noticed that cross you're wearing – are you a Christian? [If not:] Would you like to know what that cross symbolizes?
- Have you ever heard of the "Four Spiritual Laws"?
- [After some kind of Christian function:] What did you think of it? Did it make sense? Would you like to hear more?
- [To an acquaintance:] Have I ever shared with you how I began my relationship with God?

Personal Application

Write down the names of 10 non-Christians for whose salvation you would like to begin praying:

"My Ten Most Wanted List"	
1.	6.
2.	7.
3.	8.
4.	9.
5.	10.

➤ Commit to praying for the above people on a regular basis.

➤ Stay alert for "divine appointments" that God may set up for you with them. These are times when God arranges for you to spend time with one of the people you've been praying for; He's prepared his heart, and now, He's waiting for you to open your mouth so He can talk to him!

> **For Further Insight:**
> A good prayer to pray for your non-Christian friends can be found in **Ephesians 1:17-19**.

Scripture Memory Verse:

> **The Witnessing Connection—**
> "I am not ashamed of the gospel, because it is the power of God for the salvation of everyone who believes: first for the Jew, then for the Gentile."
> —**Romans 1:16**

> **WRAP UP:**
> Jesus asks you, "Will you tell others about Me?"

---

1 Story from Chuck Clark's devotional emails: "Paraclete." To subscribe: ParacleteLetter-subscribe@yahoogroups.com.
2 Bright, William R., *How To Introduce Others To Christ* (Transferable Concept #6) (Orlando, FL: New Life Publications, 1972,1992), p. 8.
3 Brown, Colin (Ed.), *The New Int'l Dictionary of New Testament Theology* (Grand Rapids, MI: Zondervan, 1967), Vol. 2, p. 109ff.
4 Skinner, Betty Lee, *Daws* (Grand Rapids, MI: Zondervan, 1974), p. 189.

The Warfare Connection...
...Dealing With Our Adversary

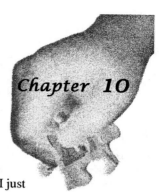

Chapter 10

Why Make This Connection?

"What a *lovely* time we're going to have on this cruise," Martin exclaimed to his wife. "I just can't wait to play shuffleboard on the deck with the sea wind blowing in my face!"

"Oh yes, Martin," Maude enthused. "What I'm looking forward to are those *sumptuous* banquets! I wonder if the captain will invite us to sit at his table for one of the meals."

"I'm sure he will," Martin replied. "And then afterwards, a little moonlight dancing on the promenade deck, perhaps?"

"Martin, you old Romeo, you! What a lovely, *lovely* time we're going to have," she sighed.

⊕   ⊕   ⊕

A couple of days later, they finally encountered the captain on the main deck.

Martin hailed him. "Oh, I say, Captain? I wonder if I might have a word with you?"

"Why, certainly. As long as it doesn't take too long. I'm rather busy, you know."

"Yes, quite," began Martin. "Well, you see, that's what we wanted to talk to you about. We've noticed that many of the personnel on this cruise seem *very* busy – sometimes too busy to attend to our needs. Very distracted, if you know what I mean. Even *rude* sometimes!"

The captain looked puzzled. "I'm not sure what you mean…"

Maude took over. "Captain, when we signed on to this cruise, we expected a little more luxury, a little more pampering. Instead of sumptuous banquets, your kitchen has been serving us C-rations! Instead of nice, soft deck chairs, all you offer are sand bags! It's atrocious!"

"And instead of shuffleboard," Martin added, " your recreation director keeps making us break down and reassemble deck guns. Rather nifty the first time. But after twenty, well, it's getting a bit boring…"

"But those are…"

Maude cut the captain off. "If you expect a positive report from us, you're going to *have* to do something about all those alarms and whistles going off every time something explodes. In fact, could you *please* get them to stop shooting those cannons off at all hours of the day and night? They are *so* unnerving!"

"And the kamikaze planes," Martin interjected. "I say – I've about had it with them. Those maniacs could *hurt* somebody!"

Finally, the captain understood the problem. "Folks, I don't know how you got on board this ship, or why you think it's a cruise liner. This is a *battleship,* and we are at *war!*"

There are many Christians who hold similar misconceptions about where they are. It is absolutely true that Jesus came to give you an abundant life. But it's important to know that – in a *very* real sense – there is a war raging all around us. The abundance He brings us will be in that context – at least during this era of our eternal existence. The battle we're in isn't for land or political power; it is for the eternal souls of men and women. Your thoughts, your motives, your priorities, your assets, your allegiances and your body are the disputed territories.

If we learn how to defend ourselves from our enemy, we'll be safe. And if we learn how to counterattack, we will expand God's kingdom on earth and push back the enemy's influence.

> **Prayer Seed:**
> "Father, my desire is to please You in all respects. But I have an enemy who opposes that desire. His objective is to destroy me. But Your power exceeds his by infinity! Teach me to wage war, so that I might defend myself, and push back his dark kingdom. Amen."

> "I submit that in our Christian anthropology we have lost something vital… There has been lost the sense of a cosmic battle, which emerges visibly on the stage of world events. What is at issue is the strengthening – or the weakening – of the spiritual forces of evil that are out to destroy the kingdom of Christ."[1]
> –James Stewart, Scottish Theologian

Our Adversary Described

In **2 Corinthians 2:11**, Paul referred to Satan and asserted, "…we are not unaware of his schemes." Paul wasn't, but unfortunately, most Christians nowadays *are* unaware – even fairly mature Christians. But that doesn't have to be the case with *you!* The objective of this study is to help you understand your enemy, and to know how to be victorious over his schemes.

Satan's Origin

Read **Ezekiel 28:12-19** in the Old Testament. In this passage, the Spirit of God is speaking through the prophet Ezekiel against the King of Tyre – a very devilish king. In this pronouncement, He is in essence saying, "King of Tyre, your characteristics are just like Satan's – now let me tell you *his* history – and his destiny…"

What was Satan like in the beginning of his existence? [See verses 12-15a, 17.]

Verse 15b says "wickedness was found" in him. What was he like after that? [See verses 16-18a.]

For more insight on Satan's sin and rebellion, read **Isaiah 14:12-17** in the Old Testament. Here God speaks through a different prophet (Isaiah) to a different king (the King of Babylon) using the same theme: "You're just like Satan – in these respects…"

Five times in this passage, Satan says, "I will." What was the primary focus of his prideful boasts – what was he "planning" to accomplish?

Verse 12 mentions the judgment of Satan's pridefulness. He had once been "the morning star," and "the son of the dawn." What was his punishment?

Jesus Christ was an eyewitness of this event. Read **Luke 10:18** in your Bible. What did He see?

The same event is mentioned in **Revelation 12:9.** In this passage, the "great dragon" is hurled to earth, but who else was sent along with him?

In our day-to-day struggles with adversity, trials and oppression, we often target fellow humans as our enemies and try to destroy *them*. But in the verse to the left (**Ephesians 6:12**), who does the Bible say are our *real* enemies – the ones that we *should* be fighting against?

Extra Insight:
God created Satan and all the angels perfect and holy. He never created evil. Satan, using his own free will, came up with that all on his own. And right from the beginning, God knew how He was going to counter it: through grace, mercy, faith and the sacrifice of His own Son, Jesus Christ.

Extra Insight: Revelation 12:4 indicates that Satan was successful in recruiting only one-third of the angels to his rebellion, leaving the great majority still loyal and obedient to God. The rebels became demons, the rest remained angels.

"For our struggle is not against flesh and blood, but against the rulers, against the authorities, against the powers of this dark world and against the spiritual forces of evil in the heavenly realms."
—**Ephesians 6:12**

Satan's Objectives and Tactics

Look up each verse in the table below and record your insights about Satan's objectives and tactics.

Passage	Here's what Satan does . . .
Matthew 4:1	*He tries to tempt people to do wrong - especially when they are in isolated places. He even tried this on Jesus!*
Matthew 4:8-10	
Luke 8:12	
Luke 13:16	
John 8:44	
2 Corinthians 11:14-15	
1 Peter 5:8	
Revelation 12:9	

> **Extra Insight:**
> Satan is not "everywhere-present" as God is. He is only one being. But he's connected to a vast network of demons who communicate with him and each other very efficiently. You will probably never deal with Satan himself, only his subordinates. But for efficiency in writing, in this study we will speak of your interaction with "his infernal kingdom" as if you were dealing with Satan himself.

Put it in plain English! Satan's lies and temptations are very subtle – and they haven't changed much in thousands of years. Examine the **Genesis 3** passage below, in which the temptation and fall of Adam and Eve are recorded. Draw a line from the underlined words of Satan on the left to what he's *really* saying from the list on the right.

Genesis 2:16-17:
    [16]And the Lord God commanded the man, "You are free to eat from any tree in the garden; [17]but you must not eat from the tree of the knowledge of good and evil, for when you eat of it, you will surely die."

Genesis 3:1-5:
    [1]Now the serpent was more crafty than any of the wild animals the Lord God had made. He said to the woman, "Did God really say, 'You must not eat from any tree in the garden'?"
    [2]The woman said to the serpent, "We may eat fruit from the trees in the garden, [3]but God did say, 'You must not eat fruit from the tree that is in the middle of the garden, and you must not touch it, or you will die.'"
    [4]"You will not surely die," the serpent said to the woman. [5]"For God knows that when you eat of it your eyes will be opened, and you will be like God, knowing good and evil."

○ "Do you mean that God – that restrictive old meanie – won't let you eat from *any* trees in the garden? I can't believe it!"

○ "Oh, don't get excited. God tends to exaggerate a lot. Let *me* give you the facts: you won't *really* die. He was just saying that to keep you under His control."

○ "Don't you see what's going on here? God doesn't want you to experience new, mind-expanding things! He's *limiting* you!"

○ "God isn't interested in associating with you – He wants to keep you ignorant and oppressed. He doesn't want you to be as smart as He is!"

Satan's Primary Tactic – Doorways & Footholds

Again, we can go all the way back to Genesis to discover how Satan works to destroy people. Find and read **Genesis 4:1-12** in your Bible. This records the birth of Adam and Eve's first two sons, Cain and Abel. Unfortunately, it also records the first murder in history – inspired by The Murderer himself. Cain and Abel had made offerings to God, and for some reason Cain's was not acceptable. We don't know exactly why – perhaps it had to do with Cain's heart attitude as he presented it. At any rate, Cain became very angry and resentful about this. God could see what was in Cain's heart and confronted him about it, giving him some very valuable advice – which Cain didn't take.

For extra insight:
see **Revelation 3:20**.

In **verse 7**, God tells Cain that if he does not do what is right, sin is crouching at his door. What do you think the "door" represents?

Why is sin crouching there? What does it desire to do?

But what did God advise Cain to do instead?

⊕   ⊕   ⊕

"In your anger, do not sin: Do not let the sun go down while you are still angry, and do not give the devil a foothold."
—**Ephesians 4:26-27**

In the verse on the left (**Ephesians 4:26-27**), it appears that anger in itself is not sin, but what we *do* when angry *can* be sin, or our anger can eventually *lead* us to sin, if we don't deal with it in a timely manner. If we let negative attitudes – sinful or not – dwell in us un-addressed, we run the risk of giving the devil a "foothold." Of what use is a foothold when climbing a cliff or a tree?

If you have a foothold, have you "conquered" the cliff or the tree? _____

Have you gotten a little closer to being able to conquer it? _____

This is a key point to remember about how Satan will try to influence your life. He won't blast in and take over all at once. He can't. But if he can get a little foothold – get you to agree to letting him have just a tiny bit of control in a small area – he's gotten just a little closer to defeating you in larger areas of your life. God's advice to you: don't give him even the first foothold! Once you've given it to him, it will be difficult to get it back!

⊕   ⊕   ⊕

"'Simon, Simon, behold, Satan has demanded permission to sift you like wheat; but I have prayed for you, that your faith may not fail; and you, when once you have turned again, strengthen your brothers.' And he said to Him, 'Lord, with You I am ready to go both to prison and to death!' And He said, 'I say to you, Peter, the cock will not crow today until you have denied three times that you know Me.'"
—**Luke 22:31-34**
[NAS]

In the verse on the left (**Luke 22:31-34**), Jesus was addressing Simon Peter the night before He was betrayed, captured, tried and crucified. Satan had apparently come before God and made an audacious demand. What was it?

What do you think that meant?

Did Jesus say, "But I told that no-good, lying, cheating murderer, 'Hands off,' gave him a good spanking and sent him on his way." – or something to that effect?

Judging from Jesus' next words, and from Peter's anguished denials of Jesus after His capture, it appears that God had to grant Satan's demand. There was something in Peter's life – perhaps his famous pride? – that had actually given Satan a legal right to come before God and demand permission to run Peter through the wringer. God sovereignly protected Peter through this trial, used it for good, and strengthened Peter by it. But it's probably an experience Peter would have rather avoided. Unfortunately, Satan used that doorway or foothold because Peter had given it to him.

Doorways and Footholds Summary

One sin doesn't throw open the door to Satan's control in your life. But it attracts him – gets his attention. He and his demonic minions are constantly looking for areas of vulnerability in your life. Is it lust? Greed? Pride? Jealousy? When he sees one, he thinks, "Hmmm. I see an inclination here. A weakness. I wonder if I can exploit it?" Then he crouches at the door, looking for ways to convince you to hold the door open for him, because he wants to *master* you, foothold by foothold.

You can slam that door shut – sending him a very loud and clear message – or you can leave it open a crack. By doing that, you're saying, "Satan, I'm open to suggestions. How would *you* meet my needs?" He'll make his proposals, and if you're foolish, you'll listen, because he'll make them sound very, very good. And if you're *really* foolish, you'll take the bait.

Instead God says, "No! *You* must master *it,* while it's still small. I'll help you, if you'll accept My help, but *you* must decide who is going to get the advantage here – My Spirit, or Satan."

⊕   ⊕   ⊕

> "If we are to be fully prepared for spiritual warfare, we must develop a bitterness towards Satan and all that he stands for. If we tolerate his advances in the slightest way, we will lose hard-earned ground that we may never gain back."
> –Gordon B. Watte

Our Authority In Spiritual Warfare

You probably have no idea what a formidable foe Satan and his demons are. He's been waging war on humans for centuries and has obviously learned a thing or two during that time. Then there's all that supernatural power he has, too. If we were to go up against him in our own power, he'd crush us like bugs.

But the Bible talks about the authority we have been given as servants of Jesus Christ. The Greek word for it is:

Exousia: "Right, power, authority, ruling power, a bearer of authority."[2]

The passage on the right has much to say about Jesus Christ's *exousia*. Whose (plural) authority does Christ's authority exceed?

> "That power is like the working of His [the Father's] mighty strength, which He exerted in Christ when He raised Him from the dead and seated Him at His right hand in the heavenly realms, far above all rule and authority, power and dominion, and every title that can be given, not only in the present age but also in the one to come. And God placed all things under His feet and appointed Him to be head over everything for the church, which is His body, the fullness of Him who fills everything in every way."
> —Ephesians 1:19b-23

And, according to the verse on the right (**Colossians 2:9-10**), who now is *also* in possession of this same fullness and *exousia?*

Read **Philippians 2:9-11** in your Bible. How many names is the name of Jesus exalted above?

How many knees must bow in obedience to that name?

> "For in Christ all the fullness of the Deity lives in bodily form, and you have been given fullness in Christ, who is the head over every power and authority."
> —Colossians 2:9-10

Your Place of Warring: There is no authority in the universe higher than Jesus Christ's. No king, no president, no demon, no angel – not even Satan himself can stand before His *exousia*. And since we are now His children, God has allowed us to operate in that same authority as we deal with the forces of darkness. As the verse to the right says, we are seated with Christ in the heavenly realms – a position of immense power and authority over our spiritual adversaries!

However, if we – through sin and disobedience – allow ourselves to slip down from our celestial power position, and once again place ourselves *under* the authority of the kingdom of darkness, our ability to wage war vanishes, and we will experience some level of defeat. This can be quickly and easily remedied through confession, repentance and the re-filling of the Holy Spirit (See Chapter 3 – *The Power Connection*).

> "And God raised us up with Christ and seated us with Him in the heavenly realms in Christ Jesus."
> —Ephesians 2:6

Never attempt spiritual warfare if you're not filled with the Spirit!

Four Fundamental Facts Regarding Adversity, Satan, Temptation and Sin

A Fail-Safe Promise:
"No temptation has seized you except what is common to man. And God is faithful; He will not let you be tempted beyond what you can bear. But when you are tempted, He will also provide a way out so that you can stand up under it."
—1 Corinthians 10:13

1 *Becoming a Christian doesn't mean you will no longer have problems; but it does mean you now have the supreme problem-solver of the universe living within you.*

Read **1 Peter 5:7-9** in your Bible. Peter's letters were definitely written to believers. He says that we need to be "self-controlled and alert." Why?

What is our adversary's ultimate objective regarding Christians (verse 8) and how should we respond to this threat (verse 9a)?

"I have told you these things, so that in Me you may have peace. In this world you will have trouble. But take heart! I have overcome the world."
—John 16:33

In the verse on the left (**John 16:33**), Jesus gives us two profound "promises" regarding Christians and adversity:

In this world, we will *definitely* _____

But we can take heart because _____

Why should both of these facts encourage us?

2 *The difficulties you will experience as a Christian will come from one of four sources...*

A. The natural consequences of foolish (but amoral) actions.

How does the first verse on the left (**Galatians 6:7**) apply to such things as: putting your thumb where the nail is supposed to be; investing in a shady company without first checking it out; marrying a habitual drug addict; jumping off a ten-story building with no parachute?

"Do not be deceived: God cannot be mocked. A man reaps what he sows."
—Galatians 6:7

"Do not love the world, nor the things in the world. If any one loves the world, the love of the Father is not in him. For all that is in the world, the lust of the flesh and the lust of the eyes and the boastful pride of life, is not from the Father, but is from the world."
—1 John 2:15-16
[NAS]

B. The temptations of Satan.

Satan's main pursuit, day and night, is to try to induce you to disobey God and line up with his agenda instead. The second passage on the left (**1 John 2:15-16**) lists three directions from which the worldly temptations of Satan will come (third sentence). List the three types of temptations, and try to think of an example of each.

1. _____ For example, when Satan says to me:

2. _____ For example, when Satan says to me:

3. _____ For example, when Satan says to me:

Read **Genesis 3:6** in your Bible. You can see Satan's same pattern in the temptation of Eve. Below, draw a line from the temptation type to the corresponding rationalization Eve used.

Think about it: Satan hasn't changed his tactics for thousands of years. Apparently, he doesn't have to!

The lust of the flesh ○   ○ Good for food

The lust of the eyes ○   ○ Pleasing to the eye

The boastful pride of life ○   ○ Desirable for gaining wisdom

C. The discipline of God as a consequence of sin.

God loves His children, and no loving father allows his kids to stray into forbidden territory without administering discipline – not to hurt them, but to give them corrective reinforcement for wrong choices. It's the same between our Heavenly Father and us.

Read **Hebrews 12:4-11** in your Bible. This passage seems to be saying that we should breathe a grateful sigh of relief when God disciplines us. Why? (See verse 8).

Will experiencing God's discipline be enjoyable? _____ But as we patiently endure God's discipline – and learn the lessons that He wants to teach us – what will result? (See verses 10-11.)

D. The testing of God designed to cause growth.

Coaches put their athletes through rigorous workouts to produce strength and endurance in them for the big competitions ahead. God puts His "athletes" through some pretty tough training too, intending to making us mature, useful, and able to withstand difficult times that may be ahead of us.

In the verse on the right (**1 Peter 5:10**), what is going to precede God restoring and strengthening us?

"And the God of all grace, who called you to His eternal glory in Christ, after you have suffered a little while, will Himself restore you and make you strong, firm and steadfast."
—**1 Peter 5:10**

When athletes suffer through grueling workouts, they focus on achieving their athletic goals to help them endure. What should Christians focus on as they experience difficult times?

"**Christianity does not remove you from the world and its problems; it makes you fit to live in it, triumphantly and usefully.**"
–Charles Templeton

3 *Adversity caused by any one of these four sources is allowed by God through a perfect blending of two Biblical principles:*
- *You will reap what you sow.*
- *God will still make good come of it.*

We already looked at **Galatians 6:7** earlier in the study (the sowing and reaping verse); now look at **Romans 8:28** on the right.

How many things will God work together for good for those who love Him? _____

Do you think this would include seemingly "bad" things as well? _____

Does this verse say that every step of the way and every event will be good? _____

So what does this tell you about the times that you encounter difficult, hurtful, trying, destructive and truly *bad* circumstances in your life?

"And we know that God causes all things to work together for good to those who love God, to those who are called according to His purpose."
—**Romans 8:28** [NAS]

A foundational law of the universe is that reaping always follows sowing. Every cause has an effect. God has instituted these laws – both physical and spiritual – in order to keep His creation running smoothly. These laws are entirely impersonal. If you break them, they'll break you, no matter who you are. If you jump off a ten-story building, you're going to come down fast, hit hard, break a lot of bones and experience a lot of pain – child of God or not. That's the reality of cause and effect, action and reaction. But God can then take this tragic, painful, "sowing and reaping" experience and work it out for the very best for those who love Him and cooperate with Him.

It's difficult to tell if God is the primary cause of a particular trial or mishap. Sometimes He is, and sometimes He isn't. But one thing you can know for sure, He will react to that trial, come to your aid, make sure it isn't more than you can bear (**1 Corinthians 10:13**), mix it with a little grace, and use it to work out His absolutely perfect plans – for you and for His kingdom.

4 Christians are to flee temptation and resist the devil.

Some Christians get this backwards, and think we are to "flee from the devil" and "resist temptation" – the opposite of what the Bible says to do!

Fleeing Temptation.
In the first passage on the left (**Proverbs 4:14-15**), what are we told to do when we come upon an opportunity that could lead us into sin?

"Do not set foot on the path of the wicked or walk in the way of evil men. Avoid it, do not travel on it; turn from it and go on your way."
—Proverbs 4:14-15

In the second verse (**2 Timothy 2:22**), do you get the idea that we should stand and fight our youthful lusts, or quickly change our location and direction and put our efforts into other pursuits?

"Flee the evil desires of youth, and pursue righteousness faith, love and peace, along with those who call on the Lord out of a pure heart."
—2 Timothy 2:22

Why do you think we are commanded to take such a "cowardly" attitude toward the temptations we come across by running away from them as if they are some insurmountable foe?

Resisting The Devil.
Satan, on the other hand, is not to be fled from, but to be actively *resisted*. We don't run from him or his minions, we stay and fight. But you'll notice in **James 4:7** that we don't have to thrash him to within an inch of his life. We only need to resist him, and the promise from God's Word is that he will flee from *us!*

"Submit yourselves then, to God. Resist the devil, and he will flee from you."
—James 4:7

Find **Ephesians 6:10-18** in your Bible. Notice that we are instructed to put on our armor. Normally, why do people put on armor?

Consider each piece of armor we are instructed to "put on." In the right column, jot down any thoughts you might have concerning why each piece is important, or what protection it is meant to give us.

Armor	Why It's Important / What Protection It Gives Us
Belt of truth	
Breastplate of righteousness	
Sandals of the preparation of the gospel of peace	
Shield of faith	
Helmet of salvation	
Sword of the Spirit – the Word of God	

A Pattern For Resisting The Devil

James 4:7-8a (the passage on the right) provides us with a good pattern we can use to resist the enemy when his activities become evident to us. Think of it in terms of how you would deal with a burglar who had broken into your house. In that case, you would probably go through four steps to "DETeR" the thief from his objectives (Detect, Empower, Trap, Reinforce) – which are the same four steps we need to take against our enemy, the Devil.[3]

> "Submit yourselves, then, to God. Resist the devil, and he will flee from you. Come near to God and He will come near to you."
> —James 4:7-8a

STEP ONE: DETECT
"We are not unaware of his schemes."
—2 Corinthians 2:11b

With A Burglar	With Satan
"I think there's a burglar in the house!"	"I think Satan is tempting me to sin!"

STEP TWO: EMPOWER
"Submit yourselves, then, to God."
—James 4:7a

With A Burglar	With Satan
Grab an "equalizer" – like a shotgun!	Spend a moment in prayer, asking God to help you fight Satan. Take your position of *"exousia"* with Christ in the heavenly realms. Be sure you're filled with the Spirit.

A suggested prayer pattern for the Empower Step: "Father, Satan is tempting me to sin against You. He wants me to lie about that situation I've been dealing with. But I desire to master *him*. Please fill me with Your Holy Spirit. I take my position seated with Christ at Your right hand in the heavenly realms – high above all principalities, powers, demonic rulers and wicked forces. With Your blessing and protection, and in Your power, I ask You to help me resist my enemy, and thereby, defeat him."

You'd be foolish to confront a burglar without some kind of an equalizer – like a shotgun or a baseball bat or something! In the same way, we are looking for trouble if we try to face the forces of darkness in our own power.

STEP THREE: TRAP

"Resist the devil and he will flee from you."
— James 4:7b

Extra Insight:
For a good index of verses you can use against specific attacks from your enemy, see Appendix #4 for your **"Spiritual Warfare Ammunition Bunker."**

With A Burglar	With Satan
Flip on the lights. "Gotcha covered! Reach for the sky or I'll shoot!"	Expose him and address him directly – just as Jesus did in **Matthew 4:1-11** – using your primary weapon: God's Word.

A suggested confrontation pattern: "Satan, I address you in the name and authority of the Lord Jesus Christ, King of kings and Lord of lords – who has bought me with His blood and made me a child of the Most High God. I am aware of your attempts to cause me to sin. In doing so, you have transgressed the commandment of God, for He has said in His Word, 'Do not steal. Do not lie. Do not deceive one another.' (**Leviticus 19:11**) You're trying to get me to lie, so *you* are in the wrong. Therefore, in the authority given to me by God Himself, I command you to cease your activities directed at me, leave me this moment, and go where Jesus Christ tells you to go."

Read **Matthew 4:1-11** in your Bible – Jesus' big confrontation with Satan in the wilderness. Notice how Jesus used *His* primary weapon. You will note that He used the same phrase three times, to counter each of the enemy's temptations. What was that phrase? (verses 4,7,10)

Look back on the listing of your spiritual armor on page 85. There are six pieces of armor listed, and five of them are defensive. What is the one offensive item listed?

STEP FOUR: REINFORCE

"Come near to God and He will come near to you."
—James 4:8a

"Your victory is based on the value of the death of Christ, a death that not only provides for salvation from the condemnation of sin, but a death that protects you from the onslaughts of the evil one."
–J. Dwight Pentecost

With A Burglar	With Satan
Call the police! Then take measures to prevent other burglars from gaining entrance the same way in the future.	After the fight, spend a short time in prayer, thanking and praising God, reading the Bible, sealing the victory and strengthening yourself.

After you have defeated your enemy, it's like a void is left there. Take a few moments to fill that void with the things of God. Read **Luke 11:24-26** to see what happens if you skip this step!

Scripture Memory Verse:

> **The Warfare Connection—**
> "Submit yourselves, then, to God. Resist the devil, and he will flee from you. Come near to God and He will come near to you. Wash your hands, you sinners, and purify your hearts, you double-minded."
> **—James 4:7-8**

WRAP UP:
Jesus asks you, "Will you fight beside Me?"

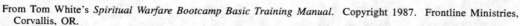

[1] From Tom White's *Spiritual Warfare Bootcamp Basic Training Manual.* Copyright 1987. Frontline Ministries, Corvallis, OR.

[2] Brown, Colin (Ed.), *The New Int'l Dictionary of New Testament Theology* (Grand Rapids, MI: Regency, 1967, '71), Vol. 2, p. 606.

[3] Illustration adapted from C.S. Lovett, *Dealing With The Devil* (Baldwin Park, CA: Personal Christianity Chapel, 1981), p. 92ff.

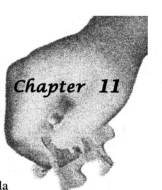

The Time Connection...
...God's Priorities Reflected In Your Calendar

Chapter 11

Why Make This Connection?

The seminar leader strode into the room with a dramatic flare. He carried only a thin manila folder and a one-gallon glass Mason jar. The attendees were intrigued.

"We're here to talk about 'Time Management'," he said with a smile. "And this jar is going to teach you one of the most important lessons you'll ever learn in your life."

The attendees were no longer merely intrigued, they were now completely focused.

"Look at this jar. Forgetting about the air that's in it, would you say it's empty or full?"

"Empty," several people responded.

"That's right. So let's fill it up." He reached behind the lectern and pulled out a box that had several fist-sized rocks in it. He carefully placed them in the jar one at a time, arranging them, rearranging them, taking some out, putting others back into the jar.

When he was satisfied, he looked up at the group and asked, "There! Now it's full, right?"

One of the attendees offered, "Well, there's still a lot of gaps between those rocks. If you had some smaller rocks you could put more in there."

"Excellent point!" the leader exclaimed, jutting his finger in the air. He then reached under the lectern and pulled out a small bucket of gravel. He put the lip of the bucket next to the jar opening and poured the gravel in. As expected, the gravel filled up the spaces between the rocks.

"Now then, we've filled up the jar, correct?"

"You know," one young woman pondered, "I'll bet if you had some sand…"

"Good idea!" So, as before, the leader reached under the lectern and brought up another small bucket, this time full of white sand. He poured it in, and it sifted down between the gravel.

"OK! Now we're done, right? All filled up!"

"Just a minute," said another man. "What about pouring some *water* in there?"

"How did I know you were going to suggest that?" the leader smiled. He produced a pitcher of water and slowly poured it in. It took a while for the water to make its way to the bottom of the jar through the dry sand, but it eventually did. He filled the jar to the brim.

"Is there anything else we could put in there?" the leader asked. No one spoke, so he then asked, "Now, relating to Time Management, what have we learned from this?"

One man's hand shot up as if he were in school, then he said enthusiastically, "If you think real hard and get creative, you can get a lot more into your schedule than you think!"

"No!" the leader responded. "That *wasn't* the point of this demonstration. You might have inferred it, but there's something even more important that you must catch."

Everyone was silent, thinking. Finally, the leader spoke, "Here's the main point: *If you want to get the big rocks in, you have to put them in first!*"

This connection will help you to identify the "Big Rocks" in your life, and ensure that *they go in first*. Then we'll consider how to put the gravel, sand and water in with the greatest amount of efficiency and impact.

Prayer Seed:
"Father, open my eyes to how I can better use my hours and days to glorify You, minister to others, manage my responsibilities and expand Your kingdom on earth. I desire times of peace and rest so that I might enjoy You and Your creation. But for the other times — make me efficient and diligent! Amen."

"The first step to managing your time should be deciding just what is important…and what isn't. Difficult as it may be, sometimes it's necessary for us to recognize that we truly *can't* do it all."[1]

—Ron Fry

Why THIS Connection?

I heard that groan! The above question may be occurring to you right now. How can something as ordinary and un-exciting as Time Management appear in the same list with such "holy" topics as Prayer, Bible Study and the Filling of the Holy Spirit? The answer is quite simple. As a new or young Christian, you have probably found out that the business of walking with Jesus *takes time*. When you received Christ, suddenly you had to try to find several additional hours in your already-full week for things like going to church, attending Bible studies, mentoring, fellowshipping and spending time alone with God. I don't know about you, but most people living in the 21st Century have already maxed-out their daily schedules. If you aren't able to organize and manage the *secular* side of your life, there will be no room for the *sacred!*

As David Dawson, founder of *Equipping The Saints* ministry has written:

"The real difficulty is not the lack of time but *what we do with the time we have*. Since we can never accumulate, stockpile, replace or turn back time, we must learn to control it as it passes. If we fail to manage our time, nothing else in our lives can or will be managed."[2]

A Critical Stewardship

Find **1 Corinthians 3:11-15** in your Bible. This is a description of a future event known as "The Judgment Seat of Christ." It is the time and place where every son and daughter of God will give an accounting of how they conducted themselves while on earth. Each of your "works" will be "tried" in order to demonstrate its quality (or lack thereof). **Note:** this is not the heaven-or-hell judgment. That verdict has already been rendered, and because of your faith in Jesus Christ, your heavenly destination is set and secure. The primary consequence of *this* judgment will be to determine your level of reward, privilege and responsibility in God's eternal kingdom.

In the **1 Corinthians 3:11-15** passage, what foundation has been laid in your life?

You are able to build on that foundation with two different classes of materials. What do you think "gold, silver and costly stones" represent?

What do you think "wood, hay or straw" represent?

Self-evaluation: Where would you place your *current* level of success with time steward-ship on the continuum below, with 5 haystacks being VERY poor, and 5 diamonds being VERY good?

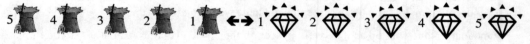

What are the hardest aspects of time stewardship for you? [Choose only 3!]

❑ Planning ahead ❑ Setting priorities ❑ Getting distracted
❑ Trying to fit too much in ❑ Not sticking to my plan ❑ Lack of diligence
❑ Procrastination ❑ Inefficiency ❑ Leaving God out of my plans
❑ Others? _____

_____

You have been entrusted with a certain amount of time in your life. It's up to you to decide what you'll exchange it for: gold, silver and costly stones, or wood, hay and straw!

"All the gold in the world cannot buy a dying man one more breath – so what does that make today worth?"
—Og Mandino

Definition of "Stewardship":
The careful and responsible manage-ment of something entrusted to one's care.[3]
Key Verse:

"As each one has received a gift, minister it to one another, as good stewards of the manifold grace of God."
—1 Peter 4:10
[NKJV]

The "Big Rocks" – Life Priorities

You may be perfectly willing to put the Big Rocks in the jar of your life first, but many people are sometimes confused about what those Rocks might be. As Christians, we want to subordinate our priorities to God's priorities, so we first need to find out what *His* are.

We can observe two of God's highest priorities in His two "Great Commandments" found in the passage on the right. What are they?

1. _____

2. _____

'God's Priorities' Brainstorming Time.
Write a summary of those two commandments at the top of the two columns below. Next, list five or six ways you could actually *do* those commands.

Commandment #1:	Commandment #2:
- Obey Him - Learn about Him	- Help the poor and needy

The activities you listed above describe ways you can make your "functional priorities" (or "actual priorities") line up with God's priorities.

Your Functional Priorities Vs. God's Priorities

It is enlightening to see how our present time investments stack up against God's priorities outlined above. We are each given 168 hours a week. How do we spend them? Examine your weekly schedule, get out your calculator and compute how much time you spend each week on each activity listed below. Write the number of hours (or portions thereof) in the blanks provided.

"The average man does not know what to do with this life, yet wants another one that will last forever."
—Anatole France

Priority Assessment Exercise: Hours/Activity

___ Sleeping	___ Car maintenance	___ Bible study (preparation and meetings)
___ Eating	___ Housework	___ Dressing, shaving, shower, make-up, etc.
___ Family time	___ Commuting	___ _____
___ Visiting with others	___ Class and homework	___ _____
___ Relaxing; personal time	___ Prayer (solo and group)	___ _____
___ Exercise program	___ Church and fellowship	___ _____
___ Employment	___ Ministry	___ _____
___ House maintenance	___ Reading (books, mags)	_____ **Total Hours Accounted For**

Hours in a week (168) – Total Hours Accounted For (_____) = "Lost Time" (_____)

Assessment: Realizing that we'll always find time to do the things we feel are important, the Priority Assessment Exercise was meant to show you where your functional priorities *actually* lie, even though they may not reflect what you consider to be your *true* priorities – or God's.

Two important observations: First, consider your "lost time" sum. (If your "Total Hours Accounted For" added up to more than 168 – you're *way* too busy!). Did the number of hours surprise you, or do you feel satisfied that your unexplained "time leaks" are few?

Secondly, compare your Hour/Activity allocations with the "'God's Priorities' Brainstorming Time" lists you wrote on the previous page – which described ways you could make your functional priorities line up with God's priorities. How much of your current functional priorities could you fit into the list of God's priorities? (Circle one)

0%	10%	20%	30%	40%	50%	60%	70%	80%	90%	100%

It's important to understand that all Christians start with a flawed set of priorities. One of the primary reasons God gave us the Holy Spirit is to help us make our functional priorities gradually line up with His priorities. It doesn't happen overnight, and it's not necessarily easy. But if we'll cooperate with God, He'll bring it to pass.

'Big Rocks' Brainstorming Time. In light of what we've learned above, what are the "Big Rocks" in your life – or at least, what *should* they be? In the space below, write down six to eight high-priority activities that you want to be sure to put in your jar *first*.

Five Steps To Efficient Time Management

In order to ensure that the Big Rocks end up strategically represented in your daily calendar, it is necessary to go through a five-step process. The next portion of this study will help to guide you through those five steps.

Step 1	*Craft A Personal Mission Statement That Reflects Your Priorities*

A Personal Mission Statement simply expresses what you are currently accomplishing or hope to accomplish in your life. If you have a firm grasp on a clear Personal Mission Statement, it will help you to plan your future. Because it will give you objective criteria by which you can say "Yes" or "No" to opportunities that present themselves, you will live more efficiently in the present. Your statement probably will include needs which you feel qualified and burdened to meet. It will reflect your priorities, will be "directional" (taking you somewhere; accomplishing something), "umbrella" (encompassing all that you do), and "lifetime" (on-going; never completely accomplished and never needing to change).[4]

Personal Mission Statement Examples . . .

Chris Adsit: "To cooperate with God in His program to conform me to the image of Jesus Christ, using all my available resources to serve Him, my family, and my fellow man mainly through a fruitful ministry of disciplemaking, writing and speaking."

David Dawson, founder and director of Equipping The Saints Ministry: "To walk in daily fellowship with God and to order my life and family in accordance with the word of God so that we are daily exchanging our lives for the fulfilling of Christ's Great Commission."

Bob Biehl, founder and director of Masterplanning Group International: "To love God and my fellow man and to show this love by helping people see life with increasing clarity and know how to cope with life's pressures and challenges."

Write Yours! In the space below, write your own Personal Mission Statement. You may want to craft it on a piece of scratch paper first, then put the finished product here.

My Personal Mission Statement:

⏰ Step 2 | Determine Major Goals That Will Combine To Make the Mission Statement Functional

These are goals that you set and never change – at least not for a long, long time. They are big, long-term dreams that might take months, years or decades to achieve. Your major goals will combine to help accomplish your Personal Mission Statement. These goals could deal with some or all of the following areas of your life:

➤ Spiritual ➤ Vocational ➤ Social
➤ Physical   ➤ Financial   ➤ Political
➤ Personal   ➤ Family

What would you like to see happen within the next twenty or thirty years? What would it take for you to be able to say at the end of your life, "I have no regrets"? Raise a family? Become a commercial airline pilot? Move to France? Earn a million dollars? Compete in the Olympics?

In the space below, list the top five **Major Goals** that you would like to accomplish in your lifetime. Avoid vague goals, like "To be happy with myself" or unrealistic ones, like "To achieve sinless perfection" or "To run a three-minute mile."

1. _____

2. _____

3. _____

4. _____

5. _____

> "It's important that you be S-M-A-R-T about setting goals:
> **Specific**
> **Measurable**
> **Attainable**
> **Realistic**
> **Tangible**."[5]
> —**John Haggai**

> **Note:** These Major Goals will be referred to again in Chapter 12, *The Vision Connection.*

⏱ Step 3 | *Determine Intermediate Goals That Will Help You Reach Your Major Goals*

Intermediate Goals are stepping-stones to Major Goals. Several Intermediate goals stacked up and accomplished equal one Major Goal. For instance: one of your Major Goals might be: "To become a brain surgeon." Your first Intermediate Goal for that one would probably be "Finish college with a 3.8 G.P.A." Next, "Get accepted at Harvard Medical School." Then, "Complete Medical School," etc.

On *separate* sheets of paper, write down the top five Major Goals you came up with in Step 2, leaving a blank half-sheet beneath each one. Under each Major Goal listed, think through the specific "stepping stones" that you will need to negotiate in order to achieve it. These constitute your Intermediate Goals.

First Intermediate Goal:

In the space provided below, write down the **first** Intermediate Goal that you came up with under **each** of your five Major Goals from the previous page.

For Major Goal #1 ⇨ 1. _____

For Major Goal #2 ⇨ 2. _____

For Major Goal #3 ⇨ 3. _____

For Major Goal #4 ⇨ 4. _____

For Major Goal #5 ⇨ 5. _____

⏱ Step 4 | *Determine Short-Term Goals That Will Help You Reach Your Intermediate Goals*

The next question you have to ask yourself is: "What can I do *right now* to get the ball rolling toward that first Intermediate Goal?" Your answers will be a list of Short-Term Goals.

As Dr. Richard Furman began his studies in college to pursue his dream of becoming a surgeon, he realized during his second night of chemistry homework that his entire goal structure depended on what he did *that night*. If he did poorly that night in his studies, he could fail a test. If he failed a test, he could get a low grade for the course. If his grades were low, no medical school. No medical school, no surgeon. Conversely, if he was diligent and did well that night, the doors would continue to swing wider and wider along the way to that surgeon shingle. It all depended on how he used his immediate time. So that night, he set his first Short-Term Goal: "Set study time each day and *never* depart from it."[6]

Examine each of the five Intermediate Goals you wrote down in Step 3. On *separate* sheets of paper, list the Short-Term Goals that will help you accomplish each one. In the space below, list the Short-Term Goals that pertain to your *first* Intermediate Goal above.

For your <u>first</u> Intermediate Goal:

1st Short-Term Goal ⇨ 1. _____

2nd Short-Term Goal ⇨ 2. _____

3rd Short-Term Goal ⇨ 3. _____

4th Short-Term Goal ⇨ 4. _____

5th Short-Term Goal ⇨ 5. _____

Step 5 | Determine A Schedule That Will Accomplish Short-Term Goals and Screen Out Unnecessary Activities

The second-to-last mile in this journey is traversed when your Short-Term Goals are placed on your calendar. The last is when they are completed. "Desire accomplished is sweet to the soul!" (**Proverbs 13:19**). It's not likely you will taste that sweetness if you don't get those desires onto a timetable!

Get out your calendar. If you don't have one, *get one!* Examine each of the Short-Term Goals you came up with in Step 4. Many of them can be tied to a specific time-to-complete or deadline – **put those goals on your calendar!**

Why is this so important? It's a critical key to mastering your time – enabling you to say "no." If you schedule the activities that reflect your priority structure *first*, people won't be able to fill up your days and nights with pursuits you don't *really* value. Like the saying goes: "If you don't schedule your days, someone else will do it for you – and you probably won't like it!"

You and the Lord – not everyone else around you – need to be the ones who decide which Big Rocks go in your jar, and then how and when the gravel, sand and water are added.

🕐 🕑 🕒 🕓 🕔

Practical Time Stewardship Principles

We'll conclude this study with five general – yet very practical – principles that will help you become better equipped as a steward of the time God has given you.

1 Consult God First

Realize that, when you asked Jesus Christ to be your Lord, He took you at your word. He now expects you to *relate* to Him as your Lord, meaning that you first ask Him about what *He* would like for you to do. If you don't follow this policy, you may end up engaging in activities that lead to dead-ends and lost time – counter-productive to God's plans for you.

Find **Acts 22:6-10** in your Bible and read Paul's testimony before the riotous crowd in Jerusalem. Paul's first question to Jesus, right after He appeared to him, was "Who are You, Lord?" You have asked that same question and now know the answer. What was Paul's *second* question?

This should be our question every day – many times a day!

The verse on the right (**John 17:4**) is part of Jesus' prayer the night before He was crucified. Notice that Jesus – even though He only had about three years of public ministry – was able to complete His work. A key point here is to notice *what* work Jesus accomplished. In this verse, how did Jesus classify the work that He completed?

What are some ways you can determine if the work (or any time-consuming activity) you're engaged in is something that God has given you to do – as opposed to something you've decided to do on your own, or something others have imposed on you?

> "Learn to say no. It will be of far more use to you than to be able to read Latin."
> –Charles Spurgeon

> "We need to learn to set our course by the stars, not by the lights of every passing ship."
> –General Omar Nelson Bradley

> "I have brought You glory on earth by completing the work You gave Me to do."
> —John 17:4

God *will* help you make choices regarding how you invest your time, but only if you'll acknowledge that your life is His to command. It's less likely that He will waste time directing you if you are not willing to follow the directions He gives.

Now, God probably isn't very concerned about whether you wear blue or black socks today, or if you take one route or another to work. But He *may* be. This is why we should always have an attitude of submissive attentiveness to the possibility that He may have some input for us.

Each verse below makes an important point about why we need to consult God regarding how we invest our time. Record your observation in the right column.

Passage	Why I should consult God regarding my time use:
"Trust in the Lord with all your heart and lean not on your own understanding; in all your ways acknowledge Him, and He will make your paths straight." —**Proverbs 3:5-6**	
"Commit your works to the Lord, and your plans will be established." —**Proverbs 16:3**[NAS]	
"A man's steps are directed by the Lord. How then can anyone understand his own way?" —**Proverbs 20:24**	
"I know, O Lord, that a man's life is not his own; it is not for man to direct his steps." —**Jeremiah 10:23**	
"'For I know the plans I have for you,' declares the Lord, 'plans to prosper you and not to harm you, plans to give you hope and a future.'" —**Jeremiah 29:11**	

2 Take Time To Plan

Some people like to "fly by the seat of their pants." They figure out what they're going to do on the run – and often lack focus and accomplish little as a result. The Bible makes it clear that we should plan ahead. Consider your resources, your available time, your objectives, and then work out a logical, achievable plan. **Plan your days, weeks, months and years ahead of time!** Initiate things, rather than simply react to circumstances as they blow up around you!

Not only was Jesus Christ the Son of God, He also spent many years as a "blue-collar worker" doing carpentry. His insights were both divine and down-to-earth! From the passage on the left, why does Jesus encourage us to spend time planning our activities before we launch into them?

Paul also had definite opinions about the importance of careful planning and setting goals. In the verse to the right, how did Paul order his life? Like a runner leaving the starting line, or like a boxer in a boxing ring?

> "Therefore I do not run uncertainly – without definite aim. I do not box as one beating the air and striking without an adversary."
> —**1 Corinthians 9:26**
> [AMP]

Read **Proverbs 21:5** in your Bible. When diligent people plan, what happens?

…and what does "haste" lead to?

3 Be Diligent

Webster's Dictionary defines *diligent* as "characterized by steady, earnest, and energetic effort; painstaking." A person can make all the plans he wants, but if there is no diligent follow-through, it's all for nothing. In the passage on the right (**Colossians 3:23-24**), what is one important reason why we should be diligent in all that we do?

> "Whatever you do, work at it with all your heart, as working for the Lord, not for men, since you know that you will receive an inheritance from the Lord as a reward. It is the Lord Christ you are serving."
> —**Colossians 3:23-24**

> "He who is faithful in a very little thing is faithful also in much; and he who is unrighteous in a very little thing is unrighteous also in much."
> —**Luke 16:10**

"Faithfulness" goes hand-in-hand with "Diligence." According to the verse on the left (**Luke 16:10**), why should we be faithful and diligent about even the small assignments God gives us?

Think About It: How would you like to add an additional eleven and a half 8-hour workdays to your year? All you have to do is get up 15 minutes earlier! Do the math. If you got up 30 minutes earlier, you'd accumulate more than three additional workweeks per year! That's probably equal to your current vacation allotment! What would you do with three extra weeks per year?

4 Pursue Efficiency

Things to consider: How can you do things better? Quicker? With greater return? Can you multiply your time by doing two things at once? Can you delegate some things?

> "Be very careful, then, how you live – not as unwise, but as wise, making the most of every opportunity, because the days are evil."
> —**Ephesians 5:15-16**

According to the verse on the left (**Ephesians 5:15-16**), why is it important that we make the most of every opportunity we are given?

What do "evil days" have to do with it?

According to the verses on the right (**1 Corinthians 14:33, 40**), what's another important reason why we should pursue efficiency and avoiding disorder?

> "For God is not a God of disorder, but of peace…. Everything should be done in a fitting and orderly way."
> —**1 Corinthians 14:33, 40**

5 *Avoid Burn-out: Get Some Rest!*

It is possible to get *too* diligent and efficient, trying to schedule every available minute for "productivity." But God makes it clear that *rest* is also an important Big Rock that we must not forget! In fact, He thought it was *so* important, He placed His thoughts on the subject in a rather conspicuous place: The Ten Commandments! Read **Exodus 20:8-11** in your Bible. First notice that God has more to say about *this* commandment than any other. What does *that* tell you? A primary facet of this commandment has to do with keeping the Sabbath day "holy." But it also addresses the concept of working. What does it command us to do?

Read **Mark 6:30-31** in your Bible. Jesus had sent His disciples out on their own to minister for awhile (verse 7). They returned, gave Him their reports, and were overwhelmed with multitudes of people to whom they still needed to minister. But Jesus had other ideas. What was Jesus' next move (verse 31)?

Create "Margin." "Margin is the space that once existed between ourselves and our limits. It's something held in reserve for contingencies or unanticipated situations. As a society, we've forgotten what margin is. In the push for progress, margin has been devoured."[8] These words, written by Dr. Richard Swenson, M.D., go a long way in pinpointing the cause of much of the stress, anxiety and burn-out in many people these days – including Christians! In some cases, it may be necessary for you to do *less* now in order to do *more* later.

So, as you are filling in your calendar, be sure to schedule in some "islands of refreshing" for yourself. Take a little time each day to relax (many very productive people – including Winston Churchill, Ben Franklin and Thomas Edison – took a nap every afternoon!). Take it easy on Sunday. Schedule a day every month or two to get alone with God in a secluded place. Plan your family vacations well in advance, so they don't get crowded out. Make sure that bubble bath concoction you bought still works. Schedule a secret rendezvous with your spouse. Go for a walk in the woods. Stop and smell the roses from time to time. Be diligent and efficient about *resting!*

Scripture Memory Verse:

> **The Time Connection—**
> "Whatever you do, work at it with all your heart, as working for the Lord, not for men, since you know that you will receive an inheritance from the Lord as a reward. It is the Lord Christ you are serving."
> —**Colossians 3:23-24**

[1] Fry, Ron, *Manage Your Time* (Hawthorne, NJ: Career Press, 1994), p. 23.
[2] Dawson, David, *Equipping the Saints Notebook,* 4 Volumes (Greenville, TX: ETS Ministry, 1982), Vol. 1, Lesson 4, p. 1.
[3] Merriam Webster's Deluxe Dictionary, "stewardship" entry – p. 1808.
[4] These concepts are from Bob Biehl of Masterplanning Group International, Lake Mary, FL. <www.master-planning.com>
[5] Haggai, John, *Lead On!* (Dallas, TX: Word, 1986)
[6] Furman, Richard, *Reaching Your Full Potential* (Eugene, OR: Harvest House, 1982), p. 11.
[7] MacDonald, Gordon, *Ordering Your Private World* (Nashville, TN: Thomas Nelson, 1985), p. 41.
[8] Swenson, Richard A. *Margin* (Colorado Springs, CO: NavPress, 1992), back cover.

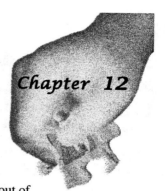

The Vision Connection...
...What God Wants To Do With Your Life

Chapter 12

Why Make This Connection?

Do you have any idea of the incredible potential God has placed in you?

Dwight was a Massachusetts farm boy, born in 1837 and poorly educated. He dropped out of school and ended up in Boston, where he found a job as a clerk in a shoe store.

Not a very auspicious beginning, so how could such a plain, low-achieving nobody every accomplish *anything* of any importance? The young man probably had no thoughts at all about "greatness" – only survival.

Dwight felt he needed some stability in his life and began going to church. There he met a man by the name of Edward Kimball who led him to Christ. Mr. Kimball – not a pastor, just another layman who attended there – spent time nurturing young Dwight in his newfound faith. Before long, a spark began to glow in Dwight's soul. – a spark of greatness.

Dwight and a few of his friends began to regularly gather in a hay field to pray together. One day, Henry Varley, a friend of Dwight's, said, "The world has yet to see what God can do with and for and through and in a man who is fully and wholly consecrated to Him."

These words fanned Dwight's spark into a flame, and nothing was able to quench it as it grew. He realized that all God needed was a person who was willing to be used – *any* person! It didn't matter if he or she was uneducated or brilliant, weak or strong, ugly or attractive. That person only needed to be willing and available.

Dwight Lyman Moody started to disciple others. For the next several years, he led Bible studies. He shared the gospel. He began to preach publicly when given the opportunity. At the age of thirty-six, he and his friend, Ira Sankey, traveled to England and held a series of evangelistic meetings. When they returned to the United States, Moody had become a national sensation. Thousands would line up to hear him talk about God.

During the next twenty-five years, Dwight L. Moody traveled over a million miles in the course of his ministry, and it is estimated that he preached to more than a hundred million people. Keep in mind, this was in the days *before* airplanes and high-tech public address systems! He established several educational institutes including Moody Bible College, and was the instigator of the Student Volunteer Movement, through which thousands of college students dedicated their lives to missionary work.

But Dwight's influence didn't stop there. While he was in England, he spent a great deal of time discipling a young man named F.B. Meyer, who later became a very popular theologian, writer and speaker. Meyer discipled the great evangelist, J. Wilber Chapman, who discipled a young baseball player named Billy Sunday, who followed in his mentor's footsteps and also became a famous evangelist during the early 1900's. Sunday discipled another anointed evangelist, Mordecai Ham, who in 1934 lead another young Billy to the Lord... Billy Graham.

Dwight L. Moody was *ordinary*. But he had simple faith in an *extraordinary* God. Dwight became great for God in this world because he cooperated with God's great plans for him. God has great plans for *you* as well! As you make this connection, God will begin expanding your vision to global proportions – and who knows? Perhaps you'll be another one of those world-changers who is "fully and wholly consecrated to Him."

Prayer Seed:
"Father, help me sense Your excitement about me and my future. I want my life to count for eternity. I want to be used by You to advance Your kingdom here on earth. But sometimes I feel so inadequate and unqualified. Help me to have *Your* confidence in me. Amen."

A succinct definition of "Vision":
"Getting on your heart what God has on His: the world."
–Dawson Trotman

What Is "Vision"?

When King Solomon wrote the words in the verse box on the left, he was referring to "revelations from God" about the present and the future. Back in his day, before most of the Bible had been written, God spoke to mankind primarily through prophets who had visions. Without them, people would not have known what God had on His mind, or what was in store for them in the future. Without this knowledge, they would neglect or eventually forget about Him altogether. But now that we have both the Old and the New Testaments, God speaks to us primarily through His Word. We can read God's thoughts and intentions any time we want! To be sure, He still reveals Himself through visions and through direct impression to our minds by the Holy Spirit. But having a copy of His eternal Word in our hands is a tremendous advantage!

God has plans for you. *Big* plans. But if you don't have any ideas about what those plans might entail, you might lose your motivation and bail out of the process He has in mind for you. You could "perish" like a seed that falls on concrete, unable to grow or reproduce. Obviously, we're not talking about eternal perishing; but as far as living a victorious life and having an impact on this world for Jesus Christ, there wouldn't be much life in you.

On the other hand, if you have "vision" – a good grasp of God's potential plans for you – you'll be more highly motivated to strap yourself in for the long-haul. The purpose of this study is to help you grasp the fact that you, yourself – not your brother, your sister, your neighbor or some superstar, – YOU have the potential of being used *significantly* by God to advance His kingdom here on earth. You may be the next Dwight L. Moody, speaking to hundreds of thousands of people, or you may be another Edward Kimball, quietly leading a Dwight L. Moody to Christ and discipling him. Either way, your impact would be global and eternal!

God's Job Description for All of His Children

The verse on the left is commonly referred to as **The Great Commission of Jesus Christ.** He spoke these words after He had been crucified, entombed, and then resurrected from the dead. He had spent about forty days with His disciples in His resurrected body, and just before He was taken up into heaven in front of His disciples (**Acts 1:1-9**), He delivered this commission.

Today's English (and Greek) Lesson. A "commission" is a command, and as such, it will be centered around an "imperative verb" – a word that tells you to *do* something, such as "*Get* me some water," or "*Throw* me the ball." As you look at **Matthew 28:19-20** on the left, see if you can spot the imperative verb in the first sentence and circle it (but be careful, it's *not* "go"). The correct answer is at the bottom of this page.

So if this is the main imperative verb of the Great Commission, on what is Christ telling us to concentrate?

❑ Making converts	❑ Making Bible study groups	❑ Making church buildings
❑ Making church-attendees	❑ Making religious programs	❑ Making choirs
❑ Making conferences	❑ Making seminaries	❑ Making pastors
❑ Making missionary agencies	❑ Making sermons	❑ Making disciples

The Point: Every one of those "makings" above is important – *vital* to the work of the Body of Christ. But we must realize that each of them (except the last one) is a *means to an end,* not the end itself. Why do you think it's important to understand the difference and focus on making disciples?

The imperative verb is the Greek word *matheteuo,* which is translated by the two English words "make disciples." Circle those two words in the Great Commission above.

What Is A Disciple?

Since it's the primary desire of our risen Savior that we should concentrate on making disciples, we had better have at least some idea of what a disciple *is* before we start the process! In this way, we can be sure that we're attempting to BE one first before we try to MAKE one.

The Greek word for disciple in the New Testament is *mathetes* which simply means "a learner, i.e., pupil."[1] But when Jesus Christ spoke of someone being *His* disciple, He meant much more than simply taking in head knowledge and storing it there. Rather, He was referring to someone who learned "by practice or experience, and acquired a custom or habit."[2]

How is an athlete who is learning a new skill out on the athletic field like a *mathetes?*

In what ways should a disciple learn like an athlete does?

Here is a useful, Bible-based definition of the word *disciple:* ⇨ "A disciple is a person-in-process who is eager to learn and apply the truths that Jesus Christ teaches him, resulting in ever-deepening commitments to Christ and to a Christlike lifestyle."[3]

From the definition above, which would you say a "disciple" is: someone who has reached a certain level of achievement, or someone who tries to consistently maintain a certain attitude?

Self-Assessment Time. Given the above definition, how much of the time would you say you were living as a true "disciple" of Jesus Christ? (Put an X on the line.)

0%	25%	50%	75%	100%

Are you satisfied with this percentage?
- ❏ No
- ❏ Somewhat
- ❏ Yes

What – if anything – do you think you should do about it?

"*Success* is the feeling you get when you reach your goals. But *significance* is making a difference in the lives of people over time."[4]
—Phil Downer

Future Development

One of the best ways you can cooperate with God's plans for you right now is to concentrate on BEING Jesus Christ's disciple. As you grow in Him, you'll be learning more about how to MAKE disciples, thereby helping to fulfill Christ's Great Commission. In preparation for this future development, make it a part of your regular prayers to ask God to develop you into a disciplemaker. The world needs what you have! That's why God put it there – and He wants it passed on to others!

What Is Important To God?

There are *lots* of things that are important to God. In the last chapter, we studied two of His highest priorities for us: Loving God and Loving our fellow man. In the context of "vision," we want to look at three other values that are important to Him. If we know the things that are important to God, it's a good first step toward making them important to us.

1 The Eternal Over the Temporal

We humans tend to place great emphasis on the here-and-now. But God, while not dismissing the temporal as totally irrelevant (after all, we *live* here!), places much greater emphasis on the eternal.

In the verse on the left (**2 Corinthians 4:17-18**), what do you think Paul is referring to when he writes of his "light and momentary troubles"? [For extra insight, check the context: verses 8-16.)

> "For our light and momentary troubles are achieving for us an eternal glory that far outweighs them all. So we fix our eyes not on what is seen, but on what is unseen. For what is seen is temporary, but what is unseen is eternal."
> —**2 Corinthians 4:17-18**

How does he compare those "troubles" with what is to come – unseen and eternal?

In the verse on the right (**John 12:24-25**), which does Jesus say is more desirable:

❑ Staying alive; enjoying the here-and-now.

❑ Producing fruit; sacrificing in this life for eternal benefits.

What do you think Jesus was talking about when He referred to the kernel of wheat "dying," and thereby producing many seeds?

> "I tell you the truth, unless a kernel of wheat falls to the ground and dies, it remains only a single seed. But if it dies, it produces many seeds. The man who loves his life will lose it, while the man who hates his life in this world will keep it for eternal life."
> —**John 12:24-25**

> "**Scripture is constantly trying to get us to look at life from the eternal perspective. Our life is but a blip on the eternal screen. Pain will be erased by a greater understanding; it will be eclipsed by a glorious result. Something so superb, so grandiose is going to happen at the world's finale that it will suffice for every hurt, atone for every heartache, and make right every injustice.**"[5]
> –**Joni Eareckson Tada**

How can we Christians involve ourselves in the eternal? The Bible tells us that, other than hell, there are only three things that are eternal They are found in the three passages listed below. Look up each scripture and write down the three eternal things.

Passage	The Eternal Thing
Psalm 90:2	
1 Peter 1:25	
1 Thessalonians 4:16-17	

To the extent that you are involved in these three eternal things, you are involved in eternity!

2 The Spiritual Over the Material

It's easy to get attached to material things, isn't it? For one thing, they're so "attachable." We can see, hear, touch, taste and smell them, and in this way they provide sensual gratification to some degree – usually immediately. But the "payback" regarding spiritual things is often intangible or deferred. Because of this, we may sometimes wonder if there even *is* any payback. However, this is what walking by faith is all about – valuing the unseen spiritual things, regardless of the payback. Jesus Christ tells us that it *will* be worth it in the long run!

In the verse on the right (**Matthew 6:19-21**), what are two reasons Jesus gives us as to why we shouldn't focus so much on amassing this world's treasures?

> [19]"Do not store up for yourselves treasures on earth, where moth and rust destroy, and where thieves break in and steal. [20]But store up for yourselves treasures in heaven, where moth and rust do not destroy, and where thieves do not break in and steal. [21]For where your treasure is, there your heart will be also."
> —**Matthew 6:19-21**

    1. (from verses 19-20)

    2. (from verse 21)

How do you think one goes about "storing up treasure in heaven"?

Find and read **Luke 12:13-21** in your Bible. In verse 15, Jesus gives us a stern warning. What is it?

In what way is His warning at odds with the prevailing sentiment regarding "possessions" in society today?

In the parable Jesus shared, a successful businessman was the focus. Was Jesus condemning his financial success, or something else? What was it?

How do you think one can become "rich toward God" (verse 21)?

Referring to the verse on the right (**Matthew 16:25-26**), how do you think someone can "save" their life in such a way that they "lose" it?

> "For whoever wants to save his life will lose it, but whoever loses his life for Me will find it. What good will it be for a man if he gains the whole world, yet forfeits his soul? Or what can a man give in exchange for his soul?"
> —**Matthew 16:25-26**

Other than actual martyrdom, how does one "lose" his life for Christ in such a way that they "find" it?

Birth of a Vision:
"After two years of marriage, Vonette and I began the ministry of Campus Crusade for Christ on a modest scale. We both had been very materialistic in our youth. But we soon came to the conclusion that serving Jesus was the most important thing in the world. So on a Sunday afternoon in the spring of 1951, Vonette and I, in our home in the Hollywood Hills, got on our knees and prayed, 'Lord, we surrender ourselves completely, irrevocably, to You. We will go wherever You want us to go and do whatever You want us to do.'"[6]

–Bill Bright

3 Availability over Ability

God doesn't need men and women of great ability. All He needs are people with availability; people who are willing and able to do what He wants them to do, say what He wants them to say, go where He wants them to go, and be what He wants them to be. He doesn't care what your background is, what challenges you are facing, or how badly you have blown it in the past. All He wants is for you to put what you have at His disposal and watch Him work through you in miraculous ways!

Read **John 6:5-13** in your Bible. There was a huge need facing Jesus and His disciples: find enough food to feed about five thousand people at a moment's notice. But there was one young boy who was *available* and offered what he had. What did he have?

And what did Jesus do with what the boy made available to Him?

What do *you* have that you would like to make available to God, and how do you think He might use it?

Below and on the next page is a brief summary of some of the great men and women of the Bible. Study the table, then **choose at least one** of these "heroes" and read their story (look up the references noted). Notice that God used them because of their *availability,* not because they were so wonderfully impressive (except in the last example on the next page). In the space provided beneath the table, write down what similarities you observed between *your* life and the life of the person you studied.

God's Heroes	Their Less-Than-Perfect Backgrounds	What God Accomplished Through Them
Abraham	Idolater (Genesis 11:26-31; Joshua 24:2); a Chaldean – people who worshipped the moon goddess, Nanna; nothing of any significance happened in his life until he was very old (Genesis 17:1-8).	Became the father of the entire nation of Israel and the human ancestor of the Savior (Genesis 12:1-3; 15:1-7).
Jacob	Grandson of Abraham. Liar, cheater (Genesis 27:1-40); chased from his homeland by his brother (Genesis 27:40-45); swindled by his uncle (Genesis 29:14b-30).	Became the progenitor of the twelve tribes of Israel (Genesis 35:22b-26) and heir to the blessings of Abraham (Genesis 28:1-4).
Joseph	Papa's pet; tattletale; hated by his brothers (Genesis 37:1-4); kidnap victim (Genesis 37:18-28); sold into slavery (Genesis 39:1); falsely accused of rape (Genesis 39:7-19); jailbird (Genesis 39:20; 41:1).	Became the prime minister of Egypt and saved the embryonic nation of Israel from extinction (Genesis 41:37-45; 45:4-13; 50:19-21).
Moses	Murderer (Exodus 2:11-12); fugitive (Exodus 2:13-15); sheepherder in exile (Exodus 2:22; 3:1); a man of great reluctance, low self-esteem, and little faith (Exodus 3:11-13; 4:1,10,13).	Became God's primary ambassador to earth, the one with whom God spoke "face to face" (Exodus 33:11); led the nation of Israel out of slavery, through the desert, and into the promised land (Exodus 4:21–20:21; 32 :1–34:35; 40:1-38).
Ruth	A Moabitess in exile, widowed, childless, destitute, homeless (Ruth 1:1-22).	God set her up with Boaz, a wealthy land-owner, and they became the great-grandparents of King David (Ruth 4:21-22).
David	Shepherd boy, youngest child of an insignificant family (1 Samuel 16:1-12); weird-looking because of his red hair and pale skin (1 Samuel 16:12).	Used by God to slay Goliath, embolden Israel (1 Samuel 17:26-53), and later to bring Israel to the pinnacle of world power (2 Samuel 7:1,18-29).

God's Heroes, continued...

God's Heroes	Their Less-Than-Perfect Backgrounds	What God Accomplished Through Them
Esther	An orphan, raised by her elder cousin; an exile in a pagan country hostile to Israel (Esther 2:5-7). Targeted along with all Jews for a holocaust (Esther 3:5-10; 4:12-14).	Became queen to King Ahasuerus (Esther 2:17) and kept Israel from annihilation (Esther 4:13-16; 7:2-10; 8:5-12).
Peter	All mouth (Matthew 26:33-35); impetuous (Matthew 17:4); puffed-up (Matthew 16:21-23); openly denied Christ in His hour of need (Matthew 26:69-75).	Became one of the all-time pillars of the early Christian church after Jesus' resurrection (Acts 2:14-41; 3:1-26; 10:1-48); wrote 1 and 2 Peter.
Paul	Vicious, zealous persecutor of Christians; sent many of God's children to prison and death (Acts 8:3; 9:1-2; 22:4-5; 26:9-11; 1 Corinthians 15:9).	Became the most influential Christian ever to have lived, spread the gospel throughout most of the known world and inspired by God to write half the books of the New Testament.
Jesus	Born in a cave-barn, a feeding trough for a crib (Luke 2:4-7); targeted for murder as an infant and exiled to Egypt as a baby (Matthew 2:1-18); raised as a carpenter's son in a backwater town in Galilee.	Made salvation available to the entire world (John 3:16) and had a greater effect on history than any other person who ever lived.

Similarities I observed between my life and the life of one (or more) of the "Heroes" above:

✧ ✧ ✧ ✧ ✧

What Are Some Of God's Important Plans For You?

In the last few pages, we considered "What Is Important To God." There is one more thing that's important to God, and that's YOU! You are *eternal*, you are *spiritual*, and you are becoming more *available* all the time. When God redeemed you from the enemy's camp, He did not intend for you to come in from the battle, get cleaned up and go sit in a recliner for the rest of the war. He redeemed you for many important reasons, not the least of which was to help Him in His plans to redeem and strengthen others.

In a study like this, we can't determine God's *specific* plans for you as an individual, but the Bible can give us some good ideas of His *general* plans. His specific plans for you will flow out of His general ones.

Read or look up the Bible passages on the left below, and write down what that verse is saying about plans God has for you as one of His children.

Passage	God plans to...
"'For I know the plans I have for you,' declares the Lord, 'plans to prosper you and not to harm you, plans to give you a hope and a future.'" **—Jeremiah 29:11**	*Make me prosperous, never harm me, and to give me hope. He's even got a future planned out for me!*
"I am the light of the world. Whoever follows Me will never walk in darkness, but will have the light of life." **—John 8:12**	

Passage	God plans to...
"Jesus said, 'If you hold to My teaching, you are really My disciples. Then you will know the truth, and the truth will set you free.'" —**John 8:31-32**	
"He tends His flock like a shepherd: He gathers the lambs in His arms and carries them close to His heart; He gently leads those that have young." —**Isaiah 40:11**	
Read **Isaiah 41:10** in your Bible.	
"And my God will meet all your needs according to His glorious riches in Christ Jesus." —**Philippians 4:19**	
Read **Ephesians 4:11-13** in your Bible.	
"He humbled you, causing you to hunger and then feeding you with manna, which neither you nor your fathers had known, to teach you that man does not live on bread alone but on every word that comes from the mouth of the Lord."—**Deuteronomy 8:3**	
"And we, who with unveiled faces all reflect the Lord's glory, are being transformed into His likeness with every-increasing glory, which comes from the Lord, who is the Spirit." —**2 Corinthians 3:18**	

What Do You Need To Do To Fit In With His Plans?

Many of the plans, promises and blessings God has for you are "unconditional," meaning they'll happen no matter what. But many of them are "conditional" – meaning they'll be realized only after certain conditions are met.

On the next page is a *very short* list of some of the conditional promises God has made to His children in His Word. It's important that you understand that God isn't some celestial Santa Clause, distributing eternal goodies to whoever happens to be standing around. There are both *benefits and responsibilities* for people of vision who desire to experience the abundant life. The verses you will be studying will help you see what you are responsible for in order to see God's plans accomplished in and through your life.

God's Conditional Promises - My Part/His Part ...

Passage	If I ...	God Will ...
"If they obey and serve Him, they will spend the rest of their days in prosperity and their years in contentment." —**Job 36:11**		
"Delight yourself in the Lord and He will give you the desires of your heart." —**Psalm 37:4**		
"Cast your cares on the Lord, and He will sustain you. He will never let the righteous fall." —**Psalm 55:22**		
"When a man's ways are pleasing to the Lord, He makes even his enemies live at peace with him." —**Proverbs 16:7**		
"Those who hope in the Lord will renew their strength. They will soar on wings like eagles; they will run and not grow weary, they will walk and not be faint." —**Isaiah 40:31**		
"Blessed are those who hunger and thirst for righteousness, for they will be filled." —**Matthew 5:6**		
"But seek first His kingdom and His righteousness, and all these things will be given to you as well." —**Matthew 6:33**		
"Whoever acknowledges Me before men, I will also acknowledge him before My Father in heaven." —**Matthew 10:32**		
"Give, and it will be given to you. A good measure, pressed down, shaken together and running over, will be poured into your lap." —**Luke 6:38**		
"And we know that in all things God works for the good of those who love Him, who have been called according to His purpose." —**Romans 8:28**		
"Humble yourselves, therefore, under God's mighty hand, that He may lift you up in due time." —**1 Peter 5:6**		

"My Legacy...
I went to a funeral to pay my respects to an old friend. Some thoughtful person had placed my friend's well-worn Bible in her hands. It looked fitting and symbolic. I could remember how her face used to light up as she'd tell others about the Lord. Yes, it was most appropriate.

Later, I was thinking: What if they always put the thing that seemed most appropriate in our hands after we die? Would it be a cigarette? A newspaper? A fishing pole? Car keys? A golf club? A worn Bible? Or even a Bible not worn at all? I just wonder what they would put in mine?"
—**Author Unknown**

Personal Application:

In this study we've learned that at the core of the Great Commission of Jesus Christ is His command that His disciples should make disciples. We've looked at three key characteristics that are important to God (eternal over temporal, spiritual over material, availability over ability). We've looked at a number of important plans God has for you, and we've studied several conditional promises that He extends to all of His children. Keeping all this in mind, go back to the Major Goals you wrote down in Chapter 11, on page 91.

Spend at least 15 minutes in quiet meditation and prayer with the Lord. Consider the Major Goals on the sheet before you. In light of what you learned in this chapter, would you want to change any of those Goals? If so, take some time to re-write them now. If not, ask God to make you a man or a woman of vision regarding those Goals. Ask Him to breathe life into those words on the paper, implant them in your heart, and give you the endurance, enthusiasm and insight you will need to pursue those Goals. Ask Him to bring other resourceful people alongside you to help you achieve them. And finally, make a proclamation to Him, to the forces of darkness who are listening, and to yourself, that your intention is for God to receive all the glory as you pursue and reach those Goals.

Scripture Memory Verse:

The Vision Connection—
"Therefore go and make disciples of all nations, baptizing them in the name of the Father and of the Son and of the Holy Sprit, and teaching them to obey everything I have commanded you. And surely I will be with you always, to the very end of the age."
—Matthew 28:19-20

"When I think of *vision*, I have in mind the ability to see above and beyond the majority. I am reminded of the eagle, which has eight times as many visual cells per cubic centimeter than does a human. This translates into rather astounding abilities. For example, flying at 600 feet elevation, an eagle can spot an object the size of a dime moving through six-inch grass. The same creature can see three-inch fish jumping in a lake five miles away. Eaglelike people can envision what most would miss."[8]
–Charles Swindoll

WRAP UP:
Jesus asks you, "Will you let Me use you in My Kingdom?"

[1] Strong, James, appendix: "Greek Dictionary of the New Testament," *Strongs Exhaustive Concordance* (Grand Rapids, MI: Associated Publishers and Authors, Inc., n.d.), p. 45.
[2] Moulton, Harold K., ed., *The Analytical Greek Lexicon Revised* (Grand Rapids, MI: Zondervan, 1981), p. 257.
[3] Adsit, Chris, *Personal Disciplemaking* (Orlando, FL: Integrated Resources, 1996), p. 35.
[4] Downer, Phil, *Eternal Impact* (Eugene, OR: Harvest House, 1997), p. 21.
[5] Tada, Joni Eareckson, "When Life Isn't Fair." *Discipleship Journal* (NavPress) Issue 89 (Sept./Oct. 1995).
[6] Bright, Bill, *Come Help Change The World* (Orlando, FL: NewLife Publications, 1999), 1999), p. 16.
[7] Swindoll, Charles, *Living Above The Level of Mediocrity* (Dallas, TX: Word Publishing, 1989), p. 144.
[8] Ibid., p. 80.

The Devotional Connection...
...Your secret life with Jesus

Why Make This Connection?

Debbie and Don had found each other. Love had blossomed, Don had proposed, and Debbie had said yes.

"I can't wait to begin our new life together, Debbie," Don said as he gazed into her eyes. "I just *know* that we're going to live happily ever after!"

"Definitely!" Debbie replied enthusiastically. "I've got it all planned out. I'm going to schedule an entire hour and a half *every Tuesday morning* to get together with you! During that time, I'm going to sing you a couple of sentimental songs, tell you that I love you, and give you a little money!"

Don looked confused. "An hour and a half? Tuesday?"

"Yep! And then, I'll sit quietly while you talk to me for 20 minutes or so. Then we'll hold hands for a minute, I'll give you a kiss, and, well, we'll do it again the next Tuesday!"

"But Debbie," Don said, "What about living together, being a couple, getting to know each other? When two people love each other and get married, they're supposed to be together more than an hour and a half a week!"

"Oh, Don!" Debbie laughed. "Don't think I'm only talking about Tuesday mornings, silly! We could talk on the phone during the other days of the week! Five or ten minutes at a time, if you want! And you could write me letters, and I'll read them and get all these warm and fuzzy feelings! It'll be great!"

"It will?" Don couldn't help wondering what Megan Smythe was doing tonight...

There are some people who look at developing a relationship with Jesus like Debbie looked at her upcoming marriage to Don. Becoming a Christian isn't like joining a club, hiring a new employee or filling out a change of address form. Jesus Christ is God, but He's also *personal*–meaning He wants to have a relationship with you like one person would have with another person. It's a lot like a marriage between two people. In fact, in several places in the Bible, Christians are collectively referred to as "the Bride of Christ."

When you received Christ into your life, you entered into a loving *relationship* with Him that will last for eternity. He already knows everything about you, but He wants you to get to know Him—and the new kingdom of which you are now part. This pursuit not only benefits you, it thrills Him! He has so much to teach you about Himself, yourself, the world, the plans He has for you, and much more. One of the best ways to cultivate your new relationship with Him is to develop a personal, intimate, secret life with Jesus.

Sure, much of your faith will be lived out in public. But when you regularly spend time alone with Him, in a place where you can focus unhindered on His word, talk with him in prayer, and listen for His voice in the quietness of your heart, the roots of your faith will reach ever-deeper, and the fruit of your life will grow ever-sweeter!

Prayer Seed:
"Father, I want to know You — not only in Your vast power and majesty, but also in the places of quietness, closeness, and intimacy, where it's just You and Me. Amen."

"You have made known to me the path of life; You will fill me with joy in Your presence, with eternal pleasures at Your right hand."
—**Psalm 16:11**

"I have loved you with an everlasting love; therefore I have drawn you with lovingkindness."
—**Jeremiah 31:3**
[NAS]

The Essence Of Eternal Life

Jesus prayed:
"Now this is eternal life: that they may know You, the only true God, and Jesus Christ, whom You have sent."
—**John 17:3**

In **John 17:3**, what did Jesus say was at the core of eternal life?

When do you think we can begin experiencing this?

How do you think we could go about this? How can a finite human being get to know the infinite God?

The Apostle Paul wrote:
"What is more, I consider everything a loss compared to the surpassing greatness of knowing Christ Jesus my Lord, for whose sake I have lost all things."
—**Philippians 3:8**

In **Philippians 3:8**, what did the Apostle Paul consider to be the greatest pursuit in his life?

Read **John 15:13-15** in your Bible. While it is true that we belong to the all-powerful, infinite God of the universe, and our desire is to worship and serve Him, we were given an incredibly elevated status when we asked Jesus to become our Savior. What is this new status we now have?

We are now His _____.

List three important aspects of maintaining a good friendship with *anybody*:

1. _____

2. _____

3. _____

"The Lord would speak to Moses face to face, as a man speaks with his friend."
—**Exodus 33:11**

Two Main OBJECTIVES In A Quiet Time

Christians down through the centuries have found it very helpful to set aside a small portion of each day to shut out the world and focus on building their relationship with the Lord. This time has been called many things: Quiet Time, Daily Devotional, The Morning Watch, Time Alone With God—but those who have made it a priority in their lives will point to it as one of the main keys to depth in their walk with Him.

"To be little with God is to be little for God."
–E. M. Bounds

An effective Quiet Time has two main functions:

1. To build a deeper relationship with God - *communication*

2. To teach you about the things of God - *education*

What do you think would be the result if a person focused only on *education* in his Quiet Time, with no thought of *communication* with God?

What if there was plenty of *communication*, but no *education*?

Two Main ELEMENTS Of A Quiet Time: Talking and Listening

1 Prayer—Talking With God

Obviously, if you're trying to develop a relationship with someone, you need to communicate with that person. As Bill Bright states so succinctly, "Prayer is simply talking to God." You don't have to be eloquent and use long, religious-sounding words. Just talk to Him, as a friend would to a friend.

According to **Philippians 4:6**, what are we encouraged to pray about?

God would prefer that we present our requests to Him rather than what?

Why do you suppose He feels this way?

Don't get the idea that prayer is all "asking." What kind of a relationship could you build with someone if all you did each time you saw that person was to ask him or her for something? Prayer shouldn't be constricted by a set "formula," but here are four ingredients of a healthy prayer life. The acrostic **ACTS** will help you remember them:

Adoration – Worshiping and praising God for Who He is; expressing our love for Him.

> *For an example, see 1 Chronicles 29:10-13.*

Confession – Admitting to God sins that He brings to your mind; asking forgiveness; seeking His cleansing.

> *For an example, see Psalm 51:1-12.*

Thanksgiving – Expressing your appreciation to God for things He has done for you.

> *For an example, see Psalm 30:1-6*

Supplication – Specific requests you have; could be for yourself or others, for spiritual, material or emotional needs or blessings. Other words used for supplication: petition, intercession (for others), making requests.

> *For an example, see 1 Kings 3:5-10*

> "Prayer is a dialogue between two persons who love each other."
> –Rosalind Rinker

> "Do not be anxious about anything, but in everything, by prayer and petition, with thanksgiving, present your requests to God."
> —Philippians 4:6

> "Each morning as I open my eyes, my first thought is, 'Good morning, Father.' At the end of my day as I lay my head on the pillow, I whisper sleepily, 'Good night, Lord.' These simple greetings acknowledge God as the Alpha and Omega of my day."
> –Lorraine Pintus

If you've been a "pray-er" for a while already, think about your current prayer life...

Do you feel you should be praying more or less?

If you feel you should be praying more, what specifically could you do about this?

On average, what percentage of your prayer times are spent in each of the four different types?

Adoration _____   Confession _____

Thanksgiving _____   Supplication _____

Are you comfortable with this mix?

If not, how do you plan to change it?

2 Bible—Listening To God

You talk to God through prayer; let Him talk to you through His Word. As you read the Bible, you will notice something very unique about it: it changes! The ink on the paper doesn't change, but how it affects you, what you learn from it, truths that pop out of it's pages— these things will be fresh and new each time you open it up! In a spiritual sense, it's *alive!* As you read it, the Holy Spirit will illumine certain things that relate specifically to you, and to where you are *right now* in your walk to maturity.

God's Word was "interactive" thousands of years before the Internet was invented! Many older Christians have read the Bible from cover to cover over a hundred times and report that it's like reading a new book each time!

Some Good Reasons To Become Bible Studiers:

1. In many places. the Bible draws vivid parallels between physical and spiritual growth. According to **1 Peter 2:2** and **Matthew 4:4**, what does the Word of God do for Christians who "internalize" it?

What do you think happens to Christians who don't spend much time studying the Bible?

2. Read **2 Timothy 3:16-17** in your Bible. Is the Bible simply an inspiring book of philosophy whose source is a group of wise and godly men? _____ If not, then how would you describe it and its source?

For further insight:
Read
2 Peter 1:16-21.

From these two verses in 2 Timothy, summarize some of the positive results of studying the Word of God.

3. When we discuss, meditate on and obey God's Word, what will result, according to **Joshua 1:8**?

"Do not let this Book of the Law depart from your mouth [in other words, don't stop talking about it!]; meditate on it day and night, so that you may be careful to do everything written in it. Then you will be prosperous and successful."
—**Joshua 1:8**

> It's not enough to simply breeze through the Bible as one would a novel. Taking time to think about what you've read, contemplating different interpretations of a passage, asking God how He might want to apply it to your life —these are facets of what we call "meditation."
>
> *Be sure to meditate on what you read!*

"Where should I start reading?"

You can start wherever you want! But if you're open to suggestions, try reading the Gospel of John first. It presents a clear picture of Jesus as the Son of God, and yet as a man who walked among us. There are considerable details regarding Jesus' personal life, His relationship with His disciples, and His relationship with His Father which you should find interesting and inspiring.

A Quiet Time Recipe?

We're hesitant to lay out a set "recipe" for your Quiet Time, but sometimes it's helpful to look at a general pattern, and then vary it to suit your own needs and desires. Here's a suggested sequence:

1. *Heart preparation.* Don't just dive into your time with Jesus head first! Take a few moments to quiet your heart before Him. You'll want to approach Him with reverence, joy and a sense of expectation.

"The Lord is in His holy temple; let all the earth be silent before Him."
—**Habakkuk 2:20**

2. *Worship.* Spend some time in praise and thanksgiving for who He is and for what He's doing in your life. Try singing some of your favorite praise songs to Him, either from memory or from a hymnal. Perhaps you could pray some of the Psalms back to Him in worship.

"Enter His gates with thanksgiving and His courts with praise; give thanks to Him and praise His name."
—**Psalm 100:4**

3. *Personal assessment.* Make sure that there isn't anything in your life that is displeasing to the Lord—this will hinder your time with Him. Ask Him to let you know if there is and take appropriate action (confession, repentance, cleansing, restitution).

4. *Time in the Word.* The dinner bell is ringing! Read/study/meditate on a section of the Bible for a good spiritual meal! How much you read will depend on how much time you have. Try to cover at least a paragraph each time. A chapter would even be better. Consider keeping a Bible Study Diary following the **SPACE** format:

> **S: Sins to confess**
> **P: Promises to claim**
> **A: Actions to avoid**
> **C: Commands to obey**
> **E: Examples to follow**

Jot down any thoughts in your diary that God places in your mind regarding *action* you should take in response to your SPACE observations. Make the verse to the right your prayer each time you open the Bible.

> **"Prayer is like fire. The fire can only burn brightly if it is supplied with good fuel. That fuel is God's Word, which must not only be studied carefully and prayerfully, but must be taken into the heart and lived out in the life."**
>
> **—Andrew Murray**

5. *Time in prayer.* You'll probably be conversing with God throughout your time in the Bible—responding to what you read—but now it's time to share your heart with Him in a more focused fashion. You may feel led to spend additional time in "Adoration, Confession and Thanksgiving," or move right into "Supplication." Remember, you can pray about *anything* (**Philippians 4:6**): family members, your job, your spiritual growth, friends, enemies, non-Christians you know, your pastor, missionaries, problems, joys, *whatever!* Consider keeping a Prayer Diary, noting your prayer requests and jotting down answers as they come.

6. *Commit your day to Him.* End by letting Him know that you've appreciated your time with Him, and that you want to "stay tuned" throughout the day. Ask Him to guide and protect you, and recommit yourself to Him as His servant—available for anything He wants you to do.

A FEW PRACTICAL CONSIDERATIONS . . .

When? The rule of thumb is: do it when you know you can be alert. But if you can handle it, schedule it first thing in the morning. Why? Here are a few good reasons:

- Give God the first and best part of your day as an offering.

- It makes sense to tune the violin *before* the concert; to put on your armor *before* the battle.

- Meeting with God first will set the tone of your day.

- If your Quiet Time is first on your schedule, you can be sure other things won't crowd it out.

A man brought an empty gallon glass jar to the front of a business meeting. He put several large stones in the jar and asked, "Is this jar full?" Everyone replied, "No!" The man produced a box of gravel and poured it in the jar, filling the spaces between the stones. "Now is it full?" "No!" everyone replied again. Next, the man produced a bag of beach sand, and poured it into the jar, filling the spaces between the gravel. "Now is it full?" The audience was hesitant, until one man said, "You could still pour some water in that jar." "Correct!" the man said. He produced a pitcher of water and filled it to the rim. "Now is it full?" "Yes!" the audience said. "Right," replied the man. "With regards to our daily schedule, what do we learn from this?" One man volunteered, "That you can always squeeze a little more time out of your day?" "That's what most people think, but that's not the point here." No one spoke for a while, so the man finally said, "If you want to get the big rocks in, you'd better put them in *first*."

Your secret time with Jesus is a
VERY big and important rock. Put it in first!

How often? It depends how vital you think your secret time with Jesus actually is. Most mature Christians would consider it *extremely* vital—on the same level as eating, sleeping, breathing and brushing your teeth. We do vital things every day. So, if getting time with Jesus is vital, it should be done daily, too. You may have to skip a day occasionally, and that's OK! But make it a goal to have your Daily Devotions *daily!* Before long, you'll find it undesirable to start a day *without* them!

Where? Choose a place that is quiet, comfortable, secluded, and free of distraction and interruption. You may have to get creative if you live in a crowded situation, but the Lord will help you think of a place. If obvious places aren't available (your bedroom, den, office, kitchen before the rest of the household gets up), consider places like your car, garage, furnace room, a closet, storage shed, bomb shelter, etc.

How long? Why not start out with ten minutes? Most of us could agree to giving the Lord 1/144th of our day—particularly when *we* will be the major beneficiaries of that investment! Five minutes in the Bible and five minutes in prayer is a very productive way to start a day, and not too big of a rock to put into our jars. But be forewarned: before long you will probably find yourself wanting to spend *twelve* minutes. Then fifteen. Then eighteen; twenty; twenty-five…

> "Let the morning bring me word of Your unfailing love, for I have put my trust in You. Show me the way I should go, for to You I lift up my soul."
> **—Psalm 143:8**

> "He awakens me morning by morning; He awakens my ear to listen as a disciple."
> **—Isaiah 50:4b** [NAS]

> "The vigor of our spiritual life will be in exact proportion to the place held by the Bible in our life and thoughts."
> –George Mueller

> **Jesus' example:**
> "Very early in the morning, while it was still dark, Jesus got up, left the house and went off to a solitary place, where He prayed."
> **—Mark 1:35**

Should I read devotional books? As an *occasional* rut-breaker, yes. But don't get in the habit of it. The direct, undiluted Word of God is what the Holy Spirit will use most effectively to feed your soul. Why substitute pre-digested food? You need meat! But by all means, read inspirational Christian books at *other* times of the day!

Don't get in a rut! Vary your routine for a fresh experience. Take a walk in the early morning instead of sitting at a desk. If you've been in the New Testament for awhile, shift to the Old Testament. If you've regularly been doing in-depth study of passages, read several books of the Bible quickly to get a bird's-eye-view. Alter your prayer objectives. Change the length of time. Write out your prayers. Compose a praise song or poem to Jesus. Spend a whole day with the Lord.

Stick to it! Behavior specialists tell us that it usually takes most people a minimum of twenty-one days of successful attempts to establish a new habit. Prayerfully commit to a goal of having a Quiet Time every day for twenty-one days *without fail!*

Personal Application:

I plan to begin meeting with God _____ days a week at

_____ (time). My first meeting with Him will be

_____ (day) at

_____ (location). I will ask

_____ to pray with me that I can stick

with it for 21 days.

Scripture Memory Verse:

> **The Devotional Connection—**
> "As the deer pants for streams of water, so my soul pants for You, O God."
> —**Psalm 42:1**

Continuing The Connection...
...How To Make The Most Of This Section

Thought/Discussion Questions

You have been diligently working through the Bible Studies. Why would you need more? The following section is *additional* material and has two audiences:

Student

If you are doing these studies on your own, you may want to take a look at the questions and illustrations in this section. The illustrations or quotes may clarify information in the studies. The questions may stimulate deeper thinking on the points covered in the studies. If you will be discussing the studies with your mentor or in a small group, these questions are designed to be a springboard to expand the study.

Mentor or Group Leader

If you are working through this material with someone else in a one-on-one situation or in a small group, this section will be of use to you as you prepare.

Read through the questions and illustrations. Decide which of the questions would work well to stimulate further discussion with your disciple or small group. *You will not want to use all of them!* As you gain familiarity with the illustrations, you will find them useful in helping your disciple to grasp the truths presented in the study.

This section is designed to be an Assistant to you, not a Director. You may not want or need to use *any* of the material presented here. Do not feel constrained to use *all* of it.

Chapter 1

The Assurance Connection...
...How Sure Can You Be?

Thought/Discussion Questions

Main Objective of This Study:

That the new Christian would understand five key facts that he or she can be *sure* about regarding salvation. This should foster confidence that he or she has a new, eternal standing with God, and is now and forever His beloved child.

Thought/Discussion Questions:

"God has said in His Word that salvation is the present possession of all believers. Therefore it is really unbelief that would lead one to say, 'I humbly *hope* I have eternal life because I believe in Jesus.' Do no speak of humility when you are doubting God!"[2]
   –Henry A. Ironside

1. Before you became a Christian, did you have some naive or unrealistic expectations regarding what it was going to be like to receive Christ? If so, what were they?

2. Our expectations regarding the things of God should be based on what He has said to us in His Word. What would you do if you came across something in the Bible that clearly contradicted a conviction you've held for a long time?

3. In Revelation 3:20, Jesus talks about our "opening the door" to Him, and allowing Him to come into our lives. In response, He says, "I will come in and eat with him, and he with Me." What do you think He meant by that?

4. Have you ever seen that famous painting of Jesus standing in front of a door, knocking? Did you ever notice that the door has no handle on the outside where Jesus is? What do you think is the significance of this?[1]

5. Read John 1:12 again. Why wouldn't it be enough for a person to "believe in His name" and yet not "receive" Him? What would this look like? What about the other way around—what would it be like to "receive" Him, and yet not "believe in His name"?

   Illustration for John 1:12 to consider or share in a group study: Which wing of an airplane can we do without, the right or the left? Which keeps the plane up in the air? Which is more important? Obviously, both wings are vital to flight. In the same way, one needs to both "believe in" and "receive" Jesus. It's not enough to simply "believe" that Jesus is God's Son; we must also receive Him into our life as our Savior. The demons also "believe," but it doesn't change their eternal destination (James 2:19).

6. Read 2 Corinthians 5:17 again. What do you think is meant by the term "new creation"? In what way is the "new creation" new?

7. The term "born again" (see John 3:1-10) has come to mean many different things to different people. But we are most interested in what *Jesus* meant when He used the term. What do you think is the difference between the *Biblical* meaning of "born again" compared to a losing football team that is "born again" into winners, or a plain woman getting "born again" by a fashion makeover?

8. How is becoming a Christian different from joining a club?

9. The study noted that our "sins" kept us apart from God, and would eventually lead us to eternal death. What do you think is meant by the word "sin"?

Illustration about "sin" to consider or share in a group study: The word "sin" was originally a Greek archery term. When an archer shot at a target, the distance would be measured between the bullseye and where the arrow struck. This measurement was called the "sin" of the arrow. In our lives, God's perfect righteousness is the bullseye, but each one of us has missed it. Some may be hitting pretty close to it, some are way off, but all miss!

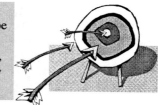

10. Psalm 103:12 says that our sins have been removed as far from us "as the east is from the west." How far is the "east" from the "west"? Do they ever meet? What does this tell you about your forgiven sins?

11. Isaiah 43:25 says that, once we have confessed our sins, God wipes them out and doesn't remember them anymore. After we have confessed and repented of a particular sin, what do you think goes through God's mind if we keep on confessing it?

12. If Christians are now "new creations," why do we continue to sin?

13. Imagine a young street urchin in 15th century England. He's homeless, constantly hungry, ignorant, illiterate and lives by thievery. One day the King notices him and takes pity on him. Since the King is childless, he decides to take the boy to his castle and adopts him as his son and heir to his kingdom. Describe the changes that this great act of grace and mercy might produce in the boy's life. How does this parallel a new Christian's life?

14. After completing point 5 on pages 4 and 5 about never again being separated from God, can you think of any other scenario that might lead to your losing your salvation that wasn't addressed by the Scriptures in this section? If so, write it down and then discuss it with some of your Christian leaders.

15. Do "feelings" have a place in the Christian life?

16. Describe a Christian's life who relies heavily on his or her feelings instead of on what the Bible says is true.

Additional materials for deeper study:

"There's a reservation in heaven with your name on it. It can't be misplaced, lost or erased. You won't get bumped because of over-booking. It is a priceless gift, guaranteed."[3]
–Steven L. Pogue

Available through New Life Resources: 1-800-827-2788:
- *Personal Disciplemaking*, Chapter 9.
- Transferable Concept #1: *How To Be Sure You're A Christian*, by Bill Bright (Campus Crusade for Christ). This is an excellent booklet to send home with a new believer. It covers the concept that becoming a Christian involves a three-fold commitment: intellectual, emotional and volitional.
- *More Than A Carpenter* by Josh McDowell (Tyndale House Publishers). Great for someone who is still not too sure about the historicity of Christianity or about the validity of Jesus' claim to be God.
- *Ten Basic Steps Toward Christian Maturity:* Introduction: The Uniqueness of Jesus. This introductory booklet to Campus Crusade for Christ's classic Bible study series is an evangelistic study, but provides a great deal of information for someone who wants a firmer grasp of what he did when he invited Christ into his life.

Other books available through your bookstore or on the web:
- *Eternal Security—Can You Be Sure?* by Charles Stanley (Thomas Nelson Publishers). Gives a very well-reasoned presentation about how a Christian can know for sure that he's saved forever—no chance of losing his salvation.

[1] There are actually two such paintings. One is by William Holman Hunt: "The Light of the World" and the other is by Warner Sallman: "Christ At Heart's Door." Both are viewable on the Internet.
[2] Ironside, Henry A., *Full Assurance* (Chicago, IL: Moody Press, 1937), p. 118.
[3] Pogue, Steven L., *The First Year Of Your Christian Life* (Orlando, FL: Integrated Resource, 1989), P. 18.

Chapter 2

The Significance Connection...
...What Happened To YOU?

Thought/Discussion Questions

Main Objective of This Study:

That the new Christian would understand in greater detail the vast scope and significance of what happened to him or her upon receiving Christ as Savior, thus producing a deeper commitment and greater motivation to go on with Christ.

Thought/Discussion Questions:

Note: Revisit the archery illustration about the word "sin" found on page 117, Thought/Discussion Questions for *The Assurance Connection.*

1. Before you completed this study, in what ways was your attitude toward the kingdom of God similar to Pierre Chanel's attitude toward the small, dusty painting he was trying to sell in that French flea market? In what ways has it changed now that you have completed the study?

2. What was the most amazing and encouraging fact you personally learned from the sixteen points highlighted in the study (four "BAD Good News" points and twelve "GOOD Good News")?

3. How were you affected as you read the four "BAD Good News" points? Do you find it offensive to be told that you were a sinner headed for hell prior to receiving Christ? Why might some people be offended by this pronouncement?

Point of Clarification on Revelation 20:11-15: Many people are apprehensive about this question: "How could a loving God send people to hell?" The Bible makes it clear that God doesn't send anybody to hell. They go there of their own free will. Jesus said in Matthew 25:41 that hell was originally created to be a place of eternal judgment only for the devil and his demonic followers, not humans. But many humans have decided to quit following God and follow Satan instead, not realizing – or not *wanting* to realize – that his final destination is hell. God's primary focus now is to do everything He can to snatch people *off* that road to eternal judgment, not to put them on it. But He must do it without violating their free will – their ability to make their own choices. See 2 Peter 3:9 for insight into God's heart on this.

4. In light of what you read in Isaiah 64:6, what do you think of the philosophy of those who compare their lives with others and say to themselves, "I'm not such a bad guy. My good deeds far outweigh my bad ones. I ought to make it into heaven."?

Illustration about the purity required to enter heaven: Mike was sharing Christ at a restaurant with a college student who couldn't understand why God separates Himself from sinful humans. Mike picked up a small packet of sugar from the table. "This is pure, unadulterated sugar, right?" "Right," the student replied. Then Mike picked up a packet of Equal™ – artificial sweetener. "Is this sugar?" "No, of course not." Mike asked, "If I were to mix the two together, wouldn't it be pure sugar then?" "No," the student said. "You can't mix two different substances and expect it to be pure." Then Mike observed, "It's the same with God. He is perfectly holy and righteous and we're not. If God were to 'mix' with us in fellowship while we were still in an unredeemed and unholy state, He would compromise His character and no longer be holy. So until we receive the righteousness of Christ through our salvation, we can't have communion with God. As much as Equal *wants* to be equal to sugar, it's not; and as much as an unsaved human *wants* to fellowship with God in holiness, he can't – apart from Christ.[1]

5. The first point in the "GOOD Good news" section was that you have been made "perfect" through the sacrifice of Jesus Christ on the cross. But do you now act perfectly? Do you drive your car perfectly? Do you spell perfectly? To what is this state of perfection referring? (See Romans 4:3-8 for additional insight into this.)

6. We've all sinned in the past. When you confess your sins to God, He forgives them, forgets them, and throws them as far away from you as the east is from the west (Psalm 103:12). But sometimes, our enemy will "play the old tapes" and remind us of our previous sins. What should we do when that happens? Should we confess them to God *again?* Why or why not?

7. Why is it encouraging to you to know that the Holy Spirit now lives in you?

8. The fourth "GOOD Good News" point refers to being "born again" (page 9). How is being born spiritually like being born physically? How are they different?

9. In "GOOD Good News" point #5 (page 10 and in Chapter 1 – *The Assurance Connection*), the conclusion was drawn that eternal life is eternal – that is, once you have it, it's impossible for you to lose it. What do you think about this; do you agree or disagree? Why?[2]

10. What are some of the "old" things that are NOT gone from your life, which you wish would be? Why do you think they are still there? (We'll deal with this subject more in Chapter 4 – The Victory Connection.)

11. The verse highlighted in point #7 (2 Corinthians 5:18 - page 11) says that we have been reconciled to God, and that He has now given to us the "ministry of reconciliation." What do you think this means?

12. Referring to Romans 5:1 in GOOD point #8 (page 11), what do you think is the difference between having peace *with* God (as it says in this verse) and having the peace *of* God?

13. As you look back over your life before you knew Christ, is it easy or difficult to believe that you were at war with God and part of Satan's rebellion against Him? Why?

14. While it is true that we were "redeemed" out of Satan's slave market (GOOD point #9 - page 11) and set free, Paul often refers to himself as a "slave" of Jesus Christ (Romans 1:1; Philippians 1:1; Titus 1:1; etc.). In what ways do you think Paul saw himself as a "slave" to Christ? Should we look at ourselves this way? (For further insight, see Romans 6:16-22.)

> **For Further Insight:**
> The Greek word *doulos* is translated variously as *slave*, *servant* or *bondservant*. A *doulos* of Christ indicates subjection without the idea of bondage.[3]

15. Now that you've been saved, your final destination is heaven – about which you undoubtedly rejoice! But what about your current location? Of what benefit is it to be living in the kingdom of God (Colossians 1:13; GOOD point #10 - page 12) here and now on planet earth? What difference does this make in your life? Is being a Christian only a matter of looking forward to "pie in the sky by-and-by"?

16. Finish this story (as it relates to GOOD point #11 - page 12): You're a ten-year-old street beggar in London in the year 1380. You haven't seen your parents in years. You live on the streets by your wits – barely scratching out an existence. Your favorite place to beg is in front of the king's palace. One day, the king's entourage drives up. As the carriage waits for the drawbridge to be lowered, the childless king looks out the carriage window and sees you. What happens next?

17. It should be comforting to know that "the angel of the Lord" is encamped around you because of your reverential respect of Jesus Christ. Does this mean that you are now impervious to any kind of harm? Under what conditions might you still experience pain or problems – even *with* your "Guardian Angel" on the job?

Additional materials for deeper study:

Available through New Life Resources: 1-800-827-2788:
- *Personal Disciplemaking*, Chapter 10.

---

[1] Illustration from Rev. Mike Buchanan, staff member with Athletes in Action.
[2] For deeper study on the subject of Eternal Security, contact Disciplemakers International for a more advanced two-part Bible study on this often misunderstood and controversial doctrine. (*RP-001 Assurance of Salvation*)
[3] Vine, W. E. *An Expository Dictionary of New Testament Words* (Old Tappan, NJ; Revell, 1940, 1966) Vol. 3, p. 347.

Chapter 3

The Power Connection...
...The Ministry Of The Holy Spirit

Thought/Discussion Questions

Main Objectives of This Study:

That the growing disciple will have a basic understanding of the ministry of the Holy Spirit, and will seek to be filled (directed and empowered) by the Holy Spirit through confession, repentance, asking and receiving His fullness.

Thought/Discussion Questions:

1. Where is the Holy Spirit right now in relation to you?

2. Do you think that most Christians understand and apply the ministry of the Holy Spirit in their lives? If not, why do you think this is?

3. Do you agree with the statement on page 15 that this "Power Connection" will be "the most important and helpful connection you'll make in your new life with God."? Why or why not?

4. Explain the difference between being "indwelt" by the Holy Spirit and "filled" by the Holy Spirit.

5. At what point does a person become "indwelt" by the Holy Spirit?

6. Can you think of some analogies that might help to explain certain aspects of the doctrine of the Trinity?

Trinitarian Analogies

1. A man may have three identities, and yet still be one person. He may be a father, a husband and a son—three distinct roles, yet a single identity.
2. Under certain conditions involving temperature and pressure, a beaker can simultaneously hold all three states of water: solid, liquid and gas. One substance, three "manifestations."
3. There are three different time periods in which I have or will exist—the past, the present and the future. But in all three, it is the same "me."
4. One day on the calendar can have significance in three separate ways: it can be a Tuesday, Groundhog Day, and my birthday.

7. What questions do you still have regarding who the Holy Spirit is, or why He came?

8. God had many objectives in mind when He sent the Holy Spirit to us (see pages 17 and 18). Review those pages and then search your heart. Are there some things that you have yet to receive or experience from the Holy Spirit? If so, what should you do about it?

9. Would you say that the filling of the Holy Spirit is a one-time occurrence, or does it happen many times?

10. Explain the concept of "spiritual breathing." When does it become necessary?

11. If it's not too personal, when was the last time you took a "spiritual breath"? Did you notice any immediate changes?

12. Why is it important to confess our sins to God? How does one go about this?

13. Galatians 5:22-23 lists the nine elements of the "Fruit of the Spirit." Which of the elements is currently most evident in your life? Which one is the least evident? What do you plan to do about it?

14. Should a new Christian expect to see full-grown "fruit" appearing in his life right away? Why or why not?

15. Which do you think is more likely to accelerate our Christian growth: depending on the supernatural empowering of the Holy Spirit as He fills us, or developing a faithful, obedient walk with God which includes regular Bible study, prayer, fellowship and witnessing?

16. When someone is "drunk with wine," as alluded to in Ephesians 5:18, he behaves in ways that are not normal for him. In the same way, when one is "filled with the Spirit," he also acts in ways that are not normal – but in a good sense! What are some "abnormal" things that you've done while filled with the Spirit?

17. How can you *know* if you're filled with the Holy Spirit?

18. How does Jesus' admonition in John 15:1-8 to "abide in Me" relate to the concept of walking in the fullness of the Holy Spirit?

19. What should one do if he or she simply doesn't "feel" filled by the Holy Spirit?

20. What if a person asks to be filled by the Holy Spirit, and there isn't any dramatic outward manifestation, emotion or experience? Should he conclude nothing happened?

Additional materials for deeper study:

Available through New Life Resources: 1-800-827-2788:
- *Personal Disciplemaking*, Chapter 11.
- *Have You Made The Wonderful Discovery of the Spirit-Filled Life?* by Bill Bright.
    A sixteen-page tract, which succinctly explains how to be filled by the Holy Spirit.
- *Transferable Concept #2:* How To Experience God's Love and Forgiveness.
- *Transferable Concept #3:* How To Be Filled With the Spirit.
- *Transferable Concept #4:* How To Walk In the Spirit, by Bill Bright.
    The *Transferable Concepts* series is a set of nine booklets that explore several foundational "How To's" of Christian living. These three "TC's" cover much of the same material as this Bible study, but go into much greater depth.
- *Ten Basic Steps Toward Christian Maturity:* Step 3: The Christian and the Holy Spirit. This is the third book of a ten-book Bible study series by Bill Bright. It covers most of the same material contained in the *Transferable Concepts,* but primarily in a fill-in-the-blank type Bible study format. Again, more in-depth than this single study.

Other books available through your local bookstores or on the web:
- *A Picture of God—3 In 1* by Marchau.
- *Acts of the Holy Spirit* by Lloyd Ogilvie.
- *Baptism and Fullness: The Work of the Holy Spirit Today* by John Stott.
- *The Divine Comforter: The Person and Work of the Holy Spirit* by J. Dwight Pentecost.
- *The Holy Spirit: The Key To Supernatural Living* by Bill Bright.
- *The Holy Spirit* by Billy Graham.
- *Experiencing the Holy Spirit* by Andrew Murray.
- *How To Be Filled With the Holy Spirit* by A.W. Tozer.
- *People of the Spirit* by Jack Hayford.
- *Person and Work of the Holy Spirit* by R.A. Torrey.
- *The Secret: How To Live With Purpose and Power* by Bill Bright.

Chapter 4

The Victory Connection...
...Neglecting Your Old Nature

Thought/Discussion Questions

Main Objectives of This Study:

That the growing disciple will understand why he continues to struggle with sin despite being a "new creation," and how walking in the fullness of the Spirit, regular times in God's Word, and habitual obedience to His promptings will result in long-term, consistent victory over temptation.

Thought/Discussion Questions:

Deeper Thoughts:
Despite what Paul wrote in Romans 7:18-24, we know from his writings elsewhere that he in no way holds that a person is not personally responsible for his own sins. See:
Romans 3:23
Romans 6:23
1 Corinthians 3:12-17
1 Corinthians 5:9-11
1 Corinthians 11:28-30
2 Corinthians 2:5-6
Galatians 2:12-14

Illustration:
A missionary translator was trying to find a word for "obedience" in the native language. This was a virtue seldom practiced among the people into whose language he wanted to translate the New Testament. As he returned home from the village one day, he whistled for his dog and it came running at full speed. An old native, seeing this, said admiringly in the native tongue, "Your dog is all ear." Immediately the missionary knew he had his term for obedience.

1. Could you identify with the "good dog/bad dog" illustration in the opening story? What do you think the Grandfather meant when he answered the boy, "The one I feed."?

2. What are some ways we feed the "bad dog"? What are some ways we feed the "good dog"?

3. At the top of page 26 where it asks you to rate your victory experience on a scale of 1 to 10, if you wrote down an 8 or higher, to what do you attribute your success in this area? If you wrote down a 3 or lower, why do you think this condition persists? Do you have any ideas about how to change it?

4. What are three ways that a person can be incorporated into a family? Read the following three passages and name the three ways you were incorporated into *God's* family:
   • John 3:3-6
   • Ephesians 1:3-7
   • Ephesians 5:22-33

5. Since you are now His child – three times over! – what do you see as some of your new responsibilities in this position?

6. If you're in a group study, share your answer to the theoretical question at the bottom of page 26, "Why should I want the Holy Spirit controlling my life?"

7. When Satan tells you, "Go my way, and it won't hardly cost you a thing," what is the truth about his offer? In what ways will it "cost you" to go his way?

8. When Satan tells you, "God is just a cosmic spoil-sport; He only wants to limit your fun," what is the truth about God's nature? Why do some people believe Satan's lie about this?

9. Before you were a Christian, you certainly must have done *some* things that were praiseworthy – not *every* thought or action was from that list in Galatians 5:19-21. In fact, some of your thoughts and actions were probably downright *righteous!* And yet you had not received your "new well" at that time. How do you explain that?

10. If you're in a group study, share your answer to the question at the bottom of page 28, which asked if you are seeing more "Spiritual fruit" in your life since you became a Christian, and how you might increase your "fruit-bearing."

11. If you're in a group study, share your responses to the question at the bottom of page 29 which asked, "Why might the farmer continue to drink from the old well rather than from the new one? How do your responses parallel why many Christians continue to draw from their old nature rather than their new nature?

12. Here's another parable for your consideration:

> A woman married a man who turned out to be a tyrant. Every day he would give her a list of things to do that day: wash the dishes, clean and dust the house, shop for groceries, wash and iron his clothes, tend the garden, prepare dinner, etc.
>
> When he returned home from work in the evening, he would check to see that she had completed her assigned chores. If she hadn't, he would complain bitterly. "I work all day for us. Can't you even do these few things for our marriage ... for our home?"
>
> The woman was, frankly, miserable.
>
> After years of marriage, the husband died. In time, she married a man who was the opposite of her previous husband – kind and gentle, never demanding a thing. Her life was filled with joy as she basked in her new husband's love.
>
> One day, as the woman was working in the kitchen, she happened across one of her first husband's list of chores. When she read it, she was surprised to realize that she was now doing even more housework than before – but the misery and drudgery were long gone. She was motivated from within, by love, to do what she needed to do.[1]

Think about how the woman's motivation changed. What difference did this make in her attitude and behavior? Now that you have a "new well" to draw from, what differences will this make in your capacity to *do* and to *be* good? What motivates you now? What motivated you before?

13. What do you think it means to be a "living sacrifice"? (Romans 12:1 – page 30).

14. Practically speaking, how can you set out to "renew your mind"? (Romans 12:2 – page 31).

15. Practically speaking, how are you going to remember to draw from the "new well" now, instead of the "old well"?

Additional materials for deeper study:

Available through New Life Resources: 1-800-827-2788:
- *Personal Disciplemaking*, Chapter 12.
- *Ten Basic Steps Toward Christian Maturity*: Step 1 – Adventure: Lesson 4.
  Step 2 – Abundant Life: Lesson 2.
  Step 6 – Obedience: Lessons 1 & 2.
- *The Discipleship Series*: Book 2, Chapter 5.
  Book 3, Chapter 1.

Other books available through your local bookstores or on the web:
- *My Heart – Christ's Home* by Robert Boyd Munger (Intervarsity).
  A classic, excellent booklet (only 28 pages – tract size) that crystallizes the issue of letting Christ be the Lord of every "room" in your life. It's been inspiring people since 1954!
- *The Fight* by John White (InterVarsity).
  Looks at the basic areas of the Christian life – prayer, Bible study, evangelism, faith, fellowship, work and guidance – and offers refreshing insights into the struggles and joys of life in Christ. 230 pages.
- *A Long Obedience In The Same Direction* by Eugene H. Peterson (InterVarsity).
  Uses the fifteen Psalms of ascent (Psalms 120-134) as a foundation for prodding and encouraging fellow travelers on the long, uphill road of Christian discipleship.
- *The Cost Of Discipleship* by Dietrich Bonhoeffer (Macmillan Publishing).
  A classic work written by a young Lutheran minister who was martyred by the Nazis. Uses the Sermon on the Mount to speak frankly about Christian obedience and commitment. Heavy sledding but incredibly rich. 344 pages.

---
[1] Illustration from Steve Douglass in *Enjoying Your Walk With God* (Here's Life Publishers, July 1989).

Chapter 5

*T*he Growth Connection...
...Actions And Attitudes To Optimize Your Development

Thought/Discussion Questions

"The conversion of a soul is the miracle of a moment; the manufacture of a saint is the task of a lifetime."

–Alan Redpath

Main Objectives of This Study:

That the disciple would have a basic and practical understanding of spiritual growth principles and be aware of the beneficial influences of time, adversity and the sovereignty of God.

Thought/Discussion Questions:

1. How do you feel about being identified with a block of marble, in need of sculpting by a master artist? Can you identify with this, or does it offend you? Why or why not?

2. In what ways are you *different* from the block of marble? In what ways are you *similar*?

3. How much of our spiritual growth depends on God, and how much of it depends on us?

Lordship of Christ

4. What comes to your mind when someone uses the phrase "The Lordship of Christ"? What comes to your mind when words like "servant," "surrendered," and "committed" are used?

5. How does "The Lordship of Christ" relate to the "Filling of the Holy Spirit" you learned about in Chapter 3?

6. What are some things that could keep Jesus Christ from being at the "hub" of your life?

7. What are some things you can do to ensure that Christ will remain at the "hub"?

Illustration for John 15:4-7 to consider or share in a group study:
To "abide" means "to remain constant in relationship to." Jesus used the analogy of a vine and its branches to illustrate the concept of abiding in Him. Have you ever observed a branch periodically unhooking from its vine, spending awhile as a pencil or a pool cue or a baseball bat, and then expecting to reattach to the vine for more nourishment? Probably not, because branches apparently know that the moment they unhook, they're not "maintaining the status quo" – they're dying. So they hang on for all they're worth! We need to cling to Jesus with that same tenacity. Our "unhooking adventures" are a lot more dangerous than they may first appear!

The Word

"Saturate yourself with the word of God. Don't worry about understanding everything you read, because you won't. Pray before you read and ask the Holy Spirit to clarify what you are reading."

–Billy Graham

8. Why do you think it is so important for a new Christian to begin reading and studying the Bible right away?

9. Try to describe what a Christian would be like who very seldom spent time reading and studying the Bible. Do you know of any Christians like that [don't name names!]? If so, what are their lives like, as far as you've been able to observe?

10. Is *reading* the only way you can take in the nourishment of the Word of God? In what other ways can it be accomplished?

11. Hebrews 4:12 describes the Word of God as "living and active." What do you think is meant by that? In what ways has God's Word shown itself to be "alive" in your life?

Prayer

12. What does love have to do with prayer?

13. What would a relationship between a husband and a wife be like if they seldom talked to each other? How about a relationship between a human and God under the same conditions?

14. What is the biggest joy you are currently experiencing regarding prayer?

15. What seems to be the biggest barrier you are currently experiencing in your prayer life?

16. Any ideas how that barrier can be lowered or eliminated?

17. Were you able to figure out the four basic types of prayer talked about in the study? If not, here are the four types – match them with their appropriate verse: Adoration (or Praise), Confession, Thanksgiving, Supplication (or Making Requests to God). Many words could be used to describe these four types of prayer, but if you use the four mentioned here, they form a memorable acronym: ACTS.

"Prayer is not overcoming God's reluctance, it is laying hold of God's willingness."
–Richard Trench

Fellowship

18. Why do you think it's so important to get a new Christian involved in a church as soon as possible after conversion?

19. What might happen to a Christian who prays, reads the Word and witnesses, but decides not to go to church?

20. What are some practical ways we can "encourage one another daily" (Hebrews 3:13)?

21. If you are in a group study, share what the pluses and minuses are of fellowshipping at church on Sunday morning versus fellowshipping in other contexts, such as at a home fellowship, on the golf course, or camping?

Witnessing

22. What are some practical ways we can witness with our lives?

23. Why isn't it enough to simply "let our light shine" and not worry about communicating the Gospel with our words?

24. What's wrong with this statement? "Well, I've never actually spoken to anybody about the Gospel where I work, but most of the people there know I'm a Christian."

"Most people are willing to pay more to be amused than to be educated."
–Robert C. Savage

25. What "information" does a person need to know when we witness to him or her with our "words"? In other words, what main points need to be included in a Gospel presentation?

Additional materials for deeper study:

Available through New Life Resources: 1-800-827-2788:
- *Personal Disciplemaking,* Chapter 13.
- *Four Spiritual Laws* booklet, pp. 14-15.
- *Ten Basic Steps Toward Christian Maturity*: Step 1 – Adventure: Lesson 4.
  Step 2 – Abundant Life: Lesson 2.
  Step 6 – Obedience: Lessons 1 - 6.
- *The Discipleship Series*: Book 1, Chapter 6.
  Book 3, Chapter 8.
- *Enjoying Your Walk With God* by Steve Douglass.
- *Five Steps to Christian Growth* by Bill Bright.
- *The First Year of Your Christian Life* by Stephen Pogue.

The Fellowship Connection...
...God Touching You Through Other Christians

Thought/Discussion Questions

Main Objectives of This Study:

That the disciple would have a basic understanding of the importance of Christian fellowship, would know and apply the principles of Biblical fellowshipping, and would attend Christian functions with the intent of establishing Christ-centered, mutually-beneficial relationships.

> "Love is an unselfish concern for another. Love freely accepts another and seeks his good."
> –Lorne Sanny

Extra Insight:
The main Greek word used in the New Testament for "fellowship" is *koinonia*, which means "association, communion, fellowship, participation."[1] In some extra-Biblical contexts it is a business term that refers to "sharing a venture."

Thought/Discussion Questions:

1. What were some of your first experiences regarding Christian fellowship? Were they mainly positive and helpful, or negative and unmotivating? If the latter, what could you do to keep new Christians who come to your fellowship from experiencing what you did?

2. What are some practical ways you can keep new Christians from feeling out-of-place when they begin coming to your church?

3. Do you feel that the church or fellowship group that you attend is like those stands of Redwoods talked about in the opening story – interlacing their roots so they could hold each other up? If not, what do you think could be done to improve the situation? If so, how can that trait be exported to other churches or fellowships?

4. What were the two commandments mentioned in Matthew 22:37-40 (page 41)? What are some things you could do to become more expert at following command #1? How about command #2?

5. Describe God's love using phrases of three words or less. [Leader: write their observations on the board.] Which of these characteristics could *we* employ in loving others?

6. What do you think this old saying means: "When love is thick, faults seem thin"? [See 1 Peter 4:8.]

7. What's the difference between loving "with words or tongue" and loving "with actions and in truth," as mentioned in 1 John 3:18? Can you think of an example of each?

8. Explain the differences between the three words for "love" in the Greek language: *Eros, Phileo,* and *Agapé* (sidebox, page 41).

9. Since there are so many "one another" verses in the New Testament, what does this tell you about the basic nature of how Christians are supposed to relate to each other?

10. Share some of your observations about what qualifies as "True Fellowship," based on the scripture passages presented (page 43).

11. How did you respond to the "What do you think?" question: "Can't Christians just get together and have fun, without always trying to figure out how to make their social interaction times 'qualify' as 'true' Christian fellowship?" (bottom of page 43).

Yes! You don't want to work so hard trying to create artificial conditions that are supposed to be helpful that you forget to have fun! But the problem currently is that when Christians get together, they rarely even think about employing the principles of Biblical fellowship. The pendulum needs to swing back the other way a little. The admonition here is simply to be sensitive to how God might want to use you in another Christian's life when you get together. The more you incorporate that mindset and the principles of Biblical fellowshipping into your thinking and your actions, the more often you'll find yourself naturally encouraging and building up your fellow Christians in the context of relaxed recreation – not to mention in the formal church context.

12. In what ways is fellowship that takes place in a church setting different from fellowship that takes place at a home Bible study? In a recreational context, like a golf match or a picnic?

13. Brainstorm about *why* it is so vital that every Christian be regularly involved in a healthy fellowship. [Leader: write their observations on the board.]

14. After reading Mark 10:42-45, and 1 Peter 5:5-6 (Characteristics of a Mature Fellowshipper - page 45), how do you feel about the notion of being a "servant," and "submitting" to others?

15. When you see something in another Christian that makes you want to criticize, get angry or lash out, what should you do? What if the characteristic you observe in that person is something overtly sinful and/or harmful?

16. Romans 12:10 exhorts Christians to "honor one another above yourselves." What are some specific ways we can do that?

17. How does James 1:19-20 relate to the fact that God made our heads with two ears and one mouth?

18. How does it make you feel to know that there is a certain amount of dysfunction in every church, and that you will most likely find yourself at odds with other Christians from time to time (page 46-47)?

19. Why do you think we are so ready to judge the shortcomings of our fellow Christians? How do you think we can eliminate this tendency?

20. How can we become more aware of the "planks" that are in our own eyes?

21. Did Jesus tell us not to attempt to remove any "specks" from our brother's eye? What were His specific instructions?

22. The point was made that Christians shouldn't reject fellowship with each other over petty doctrinal disagreements. Can you think of any cases where Christians *should* distance themselves from each other? How should the two opposing factions relate to each other?

23. Which do you like better: open rebuke or hidden love (Proverbs 27:5-6 - page 47)? How does your answer to that question square with what the wisest man ever to have lived (Solomon) said in Proverbs 9:8: "Do not rebuke a mocker or he will hate you; rebuke a wise man and he will love you"?

24. Has someone ever confronted you about something in your life that needed attention? Did they do a good job of it (surgery) or a bad job of it (decapitation)? What was the long-term effect of their rebuke?

Additional materials for deeper study:

Available through New Life Resources: 1-800-827-2788:
- *Personal Disciplemaking,* Chapter 14.
- *Four Spiritual Laws* booklet, p. 15.
- *Ten Basic Steps Toward Christian Maturity*: Introduction—The Uniqueness of Jesus: Lesson 6.
  Step 1—Adventure: Lesson 6.
- Follow-Up Series #5 *Your New Life in Relationships.*
- Transferable Concept #8: *How To Love By Faith.*

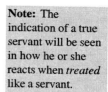

Note: The indication of a true servant will be seen in how he or she reacts when *treated* like a servant.

Attributes of the mature fellowshipper (page 45):
1. Loving
2. Patient
3. Kind
4. Faithful
5. Gentle
6. Self-controlled
7. Humble
8. Servant attitude
9. Accepts correction and reproof
10. Willing to endure hardship for others
11. Gracious in speech
12. Merciful
13. Compassionate
14. Forgiving
15. Willing to suffer wrong
16. Returns good for evil
17. Honest
18. Hospitable
19. Peacemaker
20. Generous with time, talent, treasure
21. Sensitive and aware of the needs of others
22. Seeks to build up others
23. Willing to identify, confront and help correct error in the Body
24. Recognizes, respects and appreciates spiritual leaders
25. Recognizes, respects and appreciates the gifts, talents and ministries of others
26. Desires the company of other Christians

---

[1] Brown, Colin, *The New International Dictionary of Theology Vol. 1* (Grand Rapids, MI: Regency/Zondervan, 1978), p. 639.

From *The Lost Art of Disciplemaking* by LeRoy Eims:

"[A pastor said,] 'LeRoy, it seems to me like you're some sort of a fanatic on getting people into the Word and getting the Word into their lives.'
I told him that I was not a fanatic about getting the Word of God into the lives of people and letting it dwell there richly, but rather I was a *wild-eyed* fanatic in trying to get this done! I have seen what the Word of God has done in the hearts of hundreds of people through the years and the tremendous effect it has had on their lives."

Chapter 7

*T*he Bible Connection...
...God's Nourishment For Your Soul

Thought/Discussion Questions

Main Objectives of This Study:

The disciple has a basic understanding of the importance of Biblical input, is familiar with the physical layout of the Bible, and has begun to study the Bible on his own.

Thought/Discussion Questions:

1. If you had held an opinion about something for a long time, and then found something in the Bible that apparently contradicted it, how would you respond?

2. Do you agree or disagree with this statement? "There is one book which for centuries has been recognized as the source of all books written about God, and that's the Bible." What would you say to a person of another faith who didn't agree with that statement?

3. The point was made that we need to make "The Bible Connection" in order to receive spiritual nourishment. If that's our mindset, describe how our Bible intake needs to parallel our dietary intake.

4. Consider the following two interchanges:

   #1: "You don't really have to go to work, you know. You could just stay home and starve."
   "What?!! Are you crazy? Nobody in his right mind would decide to just stay home and starve! That's ridiculous! Irresponsible! Nuts!"

   #2: "You don't really have to spend time in God's Word, you know. You could just stay away from it and starve."
   "OK. Sounds good. Wonder what's on TV tonight?"

   How can a person hold these two opposing thoughts in the same brain? To what degree does it describe *your* mindset from time to time? What could keep us from that kind of thinking?

5. In what ways is the Bible different from any other book – or collection of books – ever written?

6. Is it enough to believe that the Bible is the Word of God simply because it says it is? What is the danger in this? What other indications do we have that it truly is God's Word?

7. After reading James 2:10 (page 51), do you agree or disagree that it's not enough to observe "most" of the laws, if you're trying to get to heaven on your good works? Why or why not?

8. If this is a group study, explain to the group what are some of the major differences between the Old and New Testaments.

9. Now that the New Covenant has been ushered in by Christ's perfect sacrifice on the cross, does this mean we no longer have to obey any of the laws in the Old Testament? What about the Ten Commandments?

10. What is the most amazing thing you learned as you read about the general contents and structure of the Old Testament? Why was this so amazing to you? How about the New Testament?

11. If this is a group study, share what you wrote regarding "Jesus Christ's Opinion of the Scriptures" at the bottom of page 54.

For further insight: Read Matthew 5:17-20. What does it mean that Christ came to fulfill the law, not destroy it? And what did He mean when He said our righteousness had to exceed the righteousness of the scribes and Pharisees if we wanted to see the kingdom of heaven?

12. Why would fulfilled prophecy be an indication that the Bible is indeed the Word of God?

13. Why does the Bible's Textual Reliability give us confidence that it is the Word of God?

14. Why is it important to note that no archaeological discoveries have ever controverted any Biblical references?

15. Do you think that the Bible and modern science are in conflict? In what ways? If there is a perceived conflict, how can it be resolved? [Heavy-duty, mind-grinding question of the week:] If the Bible and science make statements that are in direct opposition to each other, which will you believe?

16. As you read through your list of "Benefits of Reading the Bible" (page 55-56), which one means the most to you personally? Why?

17. If this is a group study, share with the group some of the ways that you can be sure to "hear" the Word of God on a regular basis. What plans have you formulated for regular "reading" of the Bible?

18. If this is a group study, share some of your observations from your "Wow!/Verse/Do/Huh?" study of Psalm 1.

19. If this is a group study, discuss with your group where a new Christian should begin reading in the Bible. Genesis? Matthew? Psalms? Consider reading through portions of the Bible together as a group.

Additional materials for deeper study:

Available through New Life Resources: 1-800-827-2788:
- *Personal Disciplemaking,* Chapter 15.
- *Ten Basic Steps Toward Christian Maturity*:   Step 1 – Adventure: Lesson 5.
           Step 5 – Bible: Lessons 1-7.
           Step 7 – Witnessing: Lesson 4.
           Step 9 – Old Testament: Lessons 1-6.
           Step 10 – New Testament: Lessons 1-6.
- *The Discipleship Series*:   Book 2, Chapter 2.
           Book 5, Chapter 2.
           Book 7, all chapters.

Other books available through your local bookstores or on the web:
- For a great Bible memorization plan, contact The Navigators (1-800-366-7788) and ask for their *Beginning With Christ* Bible memory packet. Then look into their *Topical Memory System* which will help you to memorize dozens of key verses in both the Old and New Testaments in a way that links each verse to its reference and its topic. Their web site: www.navpress.com.
- For an excellent source of material regarding the validity of the Bible, get Josh McDowell's book *Evidence that Demands a Verdict,* through your local Bible bookstore, or through New Life Resources (1-800-827-2788), or through their website (www.campuscrusade.org).
- For a vast treasure trove of information regarding the scientific validity of the Bible, contact "Reasons To Believe," directed by noted astrophysicist Dr. Hugh Ross. Call them at (1-800-482-7836), or visit their web site (www.reasons.org).

Reading through the Bible in a year. If you read just three chapters a day, and five chapters on Sunday, you can read through the entire Bible in one year. In Appendix #5 is a reading schedule you may copy and use.

Suggestion: Set up a Bible Study Notebook filled with blank paper. As you study a chapter of the Bible, take one sheet of paper and write the book and chapter number at the top of the page. Divide each page into four sections where you can write out your Wow!/Verse/Do/Huh? observations. A printed form that you may copy and use is included in Appendix #5.

Chapter 8

The Prayer Connection...

...Communing With The Wisest Being In The Universe

Thought/Discussion Questions

Main Objectives of This Study:

To help the disciple gain a basic understanding of the nature of prayer, the importance of prayer, and the fundamentals of prayer; the disciple is beginning to pray on his own.

Thought/Discussion Questions:

1. In the opening story about Brian and his mother, Monica, in what ways were Brian's various actions – which seemed logical to him but, in reality, were not – like those of Christians who aren't in communication with God? How were Monica's actions like God's?

2. What's the main difference between Brian – involuntarily trapped in his world of autism – and a Christian who doesn't communicate with his Creator?

3. What were some of your first thoughts about prayer? As you look back on them now, do they seem childish and subjective, or were they pretty valid?

4. Prayer is something that seems to come naturally to just about everyone, and yet, the point was made that Christians need to be instructed in this subject. How can you resolve these two apparently opposing ideas?

5. **On Fact #1** (page 60). Did you check any of the boxes in the study, indicating that God would not be very attentive to your prayers? Has your attitude changed on that point?

6. Based on Fact #1, what is one thing that you haven't been praying about before now that you are going to begin praying for immediately?

7. **On Fact #2** (page 61). Take a personal inventory of your prayer life. If you had to assign a percentage value for how much time you currently spend in each of the four types of prayer, what would they be? (e.g., 25% Adoration, 10% Confession, etc.) Do you feel you need to make some adjustments in order to achieve a more healthy balance?

8. Think of some ways you can "adore" God in your prayer times and share them with the group.

9. Why do you think that confession of our sins is so important to God for our prayer lives?

10. **On Fact #3** (page 62). How can it be that God would actually hear every prayer prayed, when there must be millions of people praying worldwide at any given moment?

11. When you don't receive what you asked for from God, does this mean He didn't hear you? Why or why not?

12. **On Fact #4** (page 62). Why do you think God requires us to have "faith" regarding the things we pray about?

13. What if we don't have "enough" faith to believe God for what we're praying for? [Note: see Mark 9:24 for additional insight on this.]

14. Is there anything we can do that would help increase our faith? [Consider the analogy of a muscle: the greater the load you put on it, the stronger it gets.]

15. **On Fact #5** (page 63). Why doesn't God grant every request we make of Him?

16. Can you think of a time when you prayed for something, and it was granted right away? How about a time when there was a period of waiting before it was granted?

17. What possible good could have come from God denying the Apostle Paul relief from his "thorn in the flesh" (2 Corinthians 12:7-10)? What is the difference between a "thorn in the flesh" and just plain old chronic sin that we have a hard time eliminating?

18. Share your ideas on the "Hypothetical Thought" exercise (bottom of page 63).

19. **On Fact #6** (page 64). Which of the ten conditions for "Yes" answers was the most surprising to you? Why?

20. Which of the ten conditions will you have the hardest time with? What do you plan to do about it?

21. **On Fact #7** (page 65). Describe to the others in your group what it means to pray "in Jesus' name."

22. If this is a group study, share how you answered the question about coming before the Father while drunk, etc., while claiming to be coming in Jesus' name (middle of page 65).

23. **On Fact #8** (page 65). Does it seem illogical to you to have to keep coming to God with the same request? Presumptuous? Nagging? Why do you think God wants us to "keep on asking, seeking, knocking"?

24. **On Fact #9** (page 66). Why is it so important that God *not* give affirmative answers to our requests when we are unwilling to deal with known sin in our lives?

25. **On Fact #10** (page 66). How can you keep your mind from wandering while you are "listening" for God to speak to you while you're praying?

Additional materials for deeper study:

Available through New Life Resources: 1-800-827-2788:
- *Personal Disciplemaking*, Chapter 16.
- *Ten Basic Steps Toward Christian Maturity*: Step 1 –Adventure: Lesson 5.
  Step 4 –Prayer: Lessons 1-6.
  Step 7 –Witnessing: Lesson 5.

- *Discipleship Series*: Book 2, Chapter 2.
- Transferable Concept #9: *How To Pray*.
- *The Arena of Prayer* by Ben Jennings (book). Reveals prayer as God sees it and directs readers to a new, highly motivating conclusion: Prayer is "…more than something I do; it is something that God does through me."
- *Five Steps to Fasting and Prayer* by Bill Bright (Bible study booklet).
  Examines the powerful effects of fasting and prayer, and will help you and fellow group members tap into this awesome resource.

Other books available through your local bookstores or on the web:
- *With Christ In The School of Prayer* by Andrew Murray.
- *How To Pray* by R. A. Torrey.
- *The Hour That Changes The World* by Dick Eastman.
- *Power Through Prayer* by E. M. Bounds.
- *Prayer: Conversing With God* by Rosalind Rinker.
- *Prayer: Letters to Malcolm* by C. S. Lewis.
- *Intercessory Prayer* by Dutch Sheets.

"So we have to understand that although God doesn't give us what we want, He gives us what we need. What if you ask your doctor for something harmful, something he knows is harmful. You can't say he doesn't hear you when he gives to you right away something for your good. But if it's not good for you, he doesn't give it. If he contradicts your will, does that mean he hasn't heard you? Or has he heard you and does what is good for your health?"[1]
–St. Augustine

---

[1] Augustine of Hippo (AD 354-430). "Unanswered Prayer" in *Discipleship Journal* issue #62, 1991, p. 62.

Chapter 9

*T*he Witnessing Connection...
...*Spreading God's Connections Around*

Thought/Discussion Questions

Main Objectives of This Study:

That the disciple has a basic understanding of the importance of witnessing, knows the primary elements of the gospel, and can tell another person how to become a Christian.

Thought/Discussion Questions:

"Living Christianity is more than the challenge of being courageous and telling the truth. It's *equally* the challenge of being prudent, sensible and practically wise, especially in our dealings with unbelievers. [Some people ask] 'Why can't I just say it *my* way?' You can, if your goal is simple proclamation, and not persuasion."[1]
       –Tim Downs

1. How did you answer that second question on page 69, "What is the greatest thing you can do for another person?" Do you feel that most Christians feel this way? Why or why not?

2. What would you say is the biggest reason you are hesitant to share the gospel with others (assuming you are)? Do you think this reason is an unusual one or a common one? What could be done to counteract that reason?

3. **Group effort:** Without looking at your study, see how many elements of the gospel you can remember. Leader should write each element mentioned on the board or overhead projector.

4. In Bill Bright's definition of "Witnessing" in the margin of page 70, why do you think the first phrase is so important: "...taking the initiative to share the gospel..."?

5. Why is the middle phrase so important: "...in the power of the Holy Spirit..."? Why is the last phrase so important: "...leaving the results to God."? What's the alternative to "leaving the results to God," and what happens when we adopt *that* approach?

6. In the "What Is Witnessing?" section on page 70, it is mentioned that we should "be prepared to let your life be an open book to be read by anyone who wants to." Why is this a good idea? Why might it be a bad idea? What can be done to remedy the "badness" of the idea?

7. What is God's role in witnessing? How do we partner with His role – or, what is our role in light of His?

8. What role does your personal Bible study play in witnessing?

9. What is the main thing that motivates you to witness (see page 71 for your study of this)? Why is that so motivational to you?

10. What are some wrong motivations or reasons for witnessing?

11. How are the lives we live important to the successful spreading of the gospel? Generally speaking, do you think that the lives which most Christians in America are living draw people to Christ or repel them? Why do you feel this way? If there's a problem, what can be done about it?

12. On page 72, the study mentions that one facet of witnessing is that we should witness through our lives. If our objective is "two-phased" as suggested ("that they may see your good deeds *and* praise your Father," Matthew 5:16), what's wrong with feeling satisfied if we can say, "Well, I haven't really shared the gospel with my office-mates, but they all know where I stand about God and Jesus and all..."?

13. Share some of the ideas you came up with regarding specific ways you could "let your light shine before me" (middle of page 72).

14. How did you answer the last question under "Fact #2" on page 73?

Note: When someone disagrees with what is the clear teaching of Scripture, you can be sure that they're wrong, and the Bible is right! But would it be productive to force that point on the person we're witnessing to at this moment? No – it would simply start an argument. Instead, say something like this: "I don't want to debate that point with you – I'm sure you know yourself far better than I do! But let me show you what the Bible says is God's solution for those who *have* sinned and are in need of a Savior." And then proceed with your presentation. As you continue through the gospel, count on God's Word to have an effect on him – probably a much deeper one than your human arguments could ever have!

"The Word of God is like a lion. There's no need to defend a lion – just unleash it!"
–J. Vernon McGee

15. How many faithful church-attenders do you think do not have an understanding of Fact #4 on page 73? How can we help them understand it?

16. Why would it be useful to be able to share your personal testimony in two or three minutes?

17. Why would it be important to weave the gospel into your testimony presentation?

Alternative assignment: Write a letter to a non-Christian friend of yours. In your letter, share your testimony. You might start out something like this: "Joe, you're too good of a friend for me not to have shared with you what I know to be the most important thing that's ever happened to me. I hope you'll forgive me for not communicating this to you before now, and I'm praying that you might find something meaningful from what I have to share." You'll be amazed at how unthreatening the gospel contained in a testimony written in a personal letter can be!

18. How can you tell the difference between a "smoke screen" and a legitimate question?

Additional materials for deeper study:

Available through New Life Resources: 1-800-827-2788:
- *Personal Disciplemaking,* Chapter 17.
- *Four Spiritual Laws* booklet.
- *Ten Basic Steps Toward Christian Maturity:* Step 7: Witnessing.
- Transferable Concept #5: *How To Witness In The Spirit.*
- Transferable Concept #6: *How To Introduce Others To Christ.*
- *Witnessing Without Fear* by Bill Bright. A Gold-Medallion Award winning book, it offers simple, hands-on, step-by-step instruction on sharing your faith with confidence. Strongly endorsed by Billy Graham.
- *Tell It Often, Tell It Well* by Mark McCloskey. A classic by a long-time Campus Crusade for Christ leader, this book is required reading in most seminaries. It gives the reader a sensitive, informed, inoffensive approach to evangelism.
- Video training series: *Reaching Your World Through Witnessing Without Fear.* This series contains six one-hour lessons, building on Bill Bright's award-winning book. It is a high-quality series (a half-million dollars to produce!) involving drama, instruction, demonstrations, discussion, etc. Great for group training situations.

Other books available through your local bookstores or on the web:
- *Finding Common Ground* by Tim Downs. A very important, practical and extremely well thought-out book on how we can communicate with our unbelieving friends in a way that isn't pushy, judgmental or intolerant, and yet relevant. Moody Press.
- *Know Why You Believe* by Paul E. Little. A classic work that will help you "never be stumped by the same question twice." InterVarsity Press.

Asked incredulously, upon discovering his friend didn't have any gospel tracts with him: "Don't you carry anything to give to people who need the Lord? What good is a soldier without any ammunition?"[2]
–Dawson Trotman

---

[1] Downs, Tim, *Finding Common Ground* (Chicago, IL: Moody Press, 1999), p. 96.
[2] Skinner, Betty Lee, *Daws* (Grand Rapids, MI: Zondervan, 1974), p. 189.

Chapter 10

The Warfare Connection...
...Dealing With Our Adversary

Thought/Discussion Questions

Main Objectives of This Study:

To help the disciple gain a basic understanding of the fundamental facts regarding adversity, Satan, temptation and sin, and how to defend himself against spiritual oppression.

Thought/Discussion Questions:

> "Enemy-occupied territory – that's what the world is. Christianity is the story of how the rightful King has landed in disguise, and is calling us all to take part in a great campaign of sabotage."
>
> –C. S. Lewis

1. What do you think has contributed to the idea that we Christians are on "The Love Boat" rather than a battleship, as described in the opening story?

2. What evidence do you see that "there is a war raging all around us"?

3. Let's do some brainstorming so that we can help each other to "not be unaware of Satan's schemes" (2 Corinthians 2:11). In short sentences, tell me everything you currently know about our adversary. [Leader, write their responses on the board or on the overhead projector.]

4. What would you say is Satan's biggest weakness?

5. What is his greatest strength?

6. Why was Lucifer banished from heaven and cast down to earth? What was his sin?

7. What is the ultimate destination of Sata and all of his followers? [See Matthew 25:41; Revelation 20:10.]

8. When we have difficulties with other people, why is it fruitless to make *them* the object of our revenge and wrath, rather than Satan and his forces? [Ephesians 6:12.]

9. In the "Satan's Objectives and Tactics" section on page 79, which of the tactics mentioned seems to give you the most trouble? How do (or will) you counter them?

10. What should a Christian do when he realizes that sin (or Satan) is "crouching at his door," waiting for an opening to master him? What should he do if he realizes that he's "held the door open a bit" for his enemy?

11. Can you share an instance where your adversary had a foothold in your life, but you were able to "revoke" the territory you'd given him and came out victorious?

12. What has happened to you in the past when you have held on to your anger, rather than dealing with it in a godly fashion?

13. When you "slam the door" on Satan and his desire to master you, what message are you sending him? Who else are you sending a message to?

14. What do you think would happen to a Christian if he attempted to engage in spiritual warfare without assuming his position of authority and wasn't filled with the Holy Spirit?

15. What happens to Christians who don't understand that adversity is a normal part of the Christian life, who get upset every time they experience negative circumstances, wondering if they've fallen out of God's graces?

16. **Fundamental Fact #1** (page 82). 1 Peter 5:8 makes it clear that Satan's ultimate goal for Christians is to "devour" us. What does that mean? What does it look like when a Christian is "devoured"?

17. Do you think Peter wrote this warning so that we could relax and lower our guard, or is there actually a danger that we could be seriously hurt by the "roaring lion"?

18. What promise about this do we find in Isaiah 41:10?

19. **Fundamental Fact #2** (page 82). Why is it important to know which of the four sources your adversity is coming from?

20. In general terms, how would you respond differently to each of the four sources of adversity?

21. **Fundamental Fact #3** (page 83). Can you share a time when God brought good out of what was obviously a "bad" situation, in the spirit of Romans 8:28?

22. **Fundamental Fact #4** (page 84). When a person who is trying to lose weight goes to the donut shop and buys a dozen doughnuts, and then prays that God would give him strength not to eat the donuts, what part of Fundamental Fact #4 is he violating?

23. Is there some danger associated with putting on our spiritual armor and resisting the devil? How do you know? And if there is danger, what is it?

24. Regarding Step One in DETeRing the devil (page 85), what are some things you can do to make yourself better able to "Detect" the activities of your enemy?

25. Regarding Step Two, "Empower," what do you think would happen if you omitted this step, and went into battle *not* submitted to God?

26. Read **Luke 11:24-26** in your Bible. What could happen if you skip Step Four, "Reinforce"?

> **Four Fundamental Facts Regarding Adversity, Satan, Temptation and Sin.** In the companion book to this Bible study, *Personal Disciplemaking*, there are actually *Seven* Fundamental Facts mentioned. If you want to gain extra insight on this subject, familiarize yourself with the other three Fundamental Facts described in the book (pages 298-300).

> "Prayer, meditation and temptation make a minister."
> –Martin Luther

> "We are so utterly ordinary, so commonplace, while we profess to know a power the 20th century does not reckon with. But we are harmless and therefore unharmed. We are spiritual pacifist non-militants, conscientious objectors in this battle to the death with principalities and powers in high places. We are sideliners, coaching and criticizing the real wrestlers while content to sit by and leave the enemies of God unchallenged. The world cannot hate us – we are too much like its own. Oh, that God would make us *dangerous!*"
> –Jim Elliot

Additional materials for deeper study:

Available through New Life Resources: 1-800-827-2788:
- *Personal Disciplemaking*, Chapter 18.
- *Ten Basic Steps Toward Christian Maturity*: Step 2 –Abundant Life: Lessons 6,7.
    Step 4 –Prayer: Lessons 1-6.
    Step 7 –Witnessing: Lesson 5.

- *Discipleship Series:* Book 1, Chapter 2.
    Book 3, Chapter 2.

Other books available through your local bookstores or on the web:
- *The Adversary* and *Overcoming The Adversary* by Mark I. Bubeck.
- *Your Adversary The Devil* by J. Dwight Pentecost.
- *Counterattack!* by Jay Carty.
- *Victory Over The Darkness* and *The Bondage Breaker* by Neil Anderson.
- *The Beginner's Guide to Spiritual Warfare* by Neil Anderson and Timothy Warner.
- *Born For Battle* by R. Arthur Matthews.
- *The Believer's Guide To Spiritual Warfare* by Thomas B. White.

Chapter 11
The Time Connection...
...God's Priorities Reflected In Your Calendar

Thought/Discussion Questions

Main Objectives of This Study:

That the disciple has a basic understanding of the Biblical principles of successful time stewardship, prioritizing and goal-setting, and has implemented a strategy to better utilize his time.

Thought/Discussion Questions:

1. Here's a sentence for you to complete: **"When I reach 75 years old and look back over my life, I'll feel a deep sense of satisfaction if..."** Be specific in your responses.
   - Do you feel you're on a pace to reach your goal?
   - What specific things are you doing these days that will help you reach your goals?
   - What are some major things that you feel are hindering you from reaching your goals?

2. Examine the following list (or, if in a group situation, Leader write the list on the board).

1. Personal sin	6. Lack of proper training
2. Satanic opposition	7. Lack of motivation in those I minister to
3. Opposition from other people	8. No real opportunities
4. Not enough time in my days	9. Laziness on my part
5. Ignorance	10. Not enough money

   If this is a group study, take a vote. Of all the reasons listed above, which ones do the *most* to keep you from having the kind of ministry you really want to have? You may vote three times. If your group is like most groups, one of the most popular ones – if not *the* most popular – will be #4. If this is the case with you, why do you think this is such a problem for most people? Do you think most Christians recognize this as a major attack strategy of the enemy of the kingdom of God, or as just a benign hassle?

3. Relating to the "Judgment Seat of Christ" found on page 88, name a few actions that you think would qualify as "gold, silver and costly stones." Name a few actions that would be considered "wood, hay or straw."

4. If this is a group study, which of the difficult aspects of time stewardship listed on page 88 ended up being the most common among your group? What can be done about this?

5. Share some of the "functional priorities" you came up with in the "God's Priorities Brainstorming Time" exercise on page 89. Feel free to add suggestions from others to your lists.

6. Share the results of your "Priority Assessment Exercise" on page 89. Did you have a lot of "lost time," or is your life currently pretty efficient and "scheduled"? Do you think you could be *over-scheduled* and in need of more relaxation time?

7. We all have "time leaks" in our lives – activities we don't really value, but end up doing anyway. What are some common time leaks? How can we plug them?

8. What did you decide were the "Big Rocks" that need to go into your "jar" first in the exercise on page 90? Share your thoughts on this. Feel free to add or subtract from your list of Big Rocks based on what you hear from others in your group.

On Procrastination: "Have you ever stopped to wonder what the devil's favorite word might be? I've thought a lot about this and have come to the conclusion that his favorite word is 'tomorrow'."

–Hope MacDonald

9. If this is a group study, share your "Personal Mission Statement." Allow others to critique it, and see if it fits the criteria found at the bottom of page 90. How will your Personal Mission Statement be of use to you in the future?

10. Share your "Step 2 – Major Goals" from page 91. If you're in a group study, allow the other group members to give you some feedback on your goals. Are they realistic? Aiming high enough? Specific enough? Are they measurable?

11. Share what you consider to be your most exciting "Intermediate" and "Short-Term" goals. Again, have the group critique them.

12. As you consider your various "Short Term Goals," on which of them have you already started? Which, if any, have you already accomplished? Have you placed at least some of them on your calendar?

13. Do you find it difficult to say "no" when asked to do something that you know doesn't really fit in with your priorities? Why do we find this difficult sometimes? What would make it easier to be able to say "no" when we know we should?

14. At the bottom of page 93 you were asked to think of some ways to determine if your activities were God-assigned or not. Share your insights with your leader or other members of your group.

15. Are you, by nature, more of a "fly by the seat of my pants" person, or a "planner"? What are some of the advantages of planning ahead? What happens when you don't? What keeps people from taking time to plan ahead?

16. Why do you think God felt so strongly about our getting enough rest that He made it one of the Ten Commandments? What are the consequences if we continually break this "law"?

17. Where could you create some "margin" in your life?

18. If this is a group study, what other practical principles of good "Time Stewardship" have you learned over the years that you could share with the group?

Additional materials for deeper study:

Available through New Life Resources: 1-800-827-2788:
- *Personal Disciplemaking,* Chapter 19.
- *Ten Basic Steps Toward Christian Maturity:* Step 8: *Stewardship:* Lessons 1,2.
- *Managing Yourself* and *How To Achieve Your Potential* by Steven Douglass.
- *The Ministry of Management* by Steven Douglass, Bruce Cook and Howard Hendricks.

Other books available through your local bookstores or on the web:
- *Tyranny Of The Urgent* by Charles Hummel. A classic booklet that has opened people's eyes for decades about how we often allow the *urgent* to supplant the *important* things in our lives. A must-read for every growing Christian. (Meridian Publications)
- *Manage Your Time* by Ron Fry. This is one book of his seven-book series entitled *How To Study,* composed mainly for high school and college students – but helpful for us all!
- *Ordering Your Private World* by Gordon MacDonald. Recognizing that our inner spiritual world must govern the outer world of activity, MacDonald takes the reader through practical steps designed to help us organize our inner, private lives.
- *Margin* by Dr. Richard A. Swenson, M.D. Cited in this study. Helps us to restore emotional, physical, financial and time reserves in our overloaded lives.
- *Reaching Your Full Potential* by Dr. Richard Furman, M.D. Works from the premise that the pursuit of excellence in any area of life requires careful planning. It will help you recognize, set and pursue worthy lifetime goals in a practical, objective manner.

> "Though I am always in haste, I am never in a hurry, because I never undertake more work than I can go through without calmness of spirit."
> –John Wesley

Helpful Hint: When you find yourself shying away from large tasks that are *important* but not *urgent*, try the **"20 Factor"** concept from Monte Unger. We often avoid the big, important tasks because they simply seem too large to fit into our available time. The solution: break them down into smaller, bite-sized components. You may look at your disorganized garage and cringe because you know it will take hours to clean. But if you'll just give the task 20 minutes here and there, before you know it, it will be done!

Chapter 12

The Vision Connection ...
...What God Wants To Do With Your Life

Thought/Discussion Questions

Main Objectives of This Study:

That the disciple understands how valuable he is to the advancement of the Kingdom of God. Further, that he understands that God has significant plans for him, but whether or not he experiences the scope of those plans depends to some degree on his responsiveness to God and His priorities.

Thought/Discussion Questions:

"Your life on earth is a dot. From that dot extends a line that goes on for all eternity. Right now you're living *in* the dot. But what are you living *for*? Are you living for the dot or for the line? Are you living for earth or for heaven? Are you living for the short today or the long tomorrow?"[1]

–Randy Alcorn

1. Let's say that today God is sitting up in Heaven, and He gets out a big clipboard, sharpens a pencil, looks down at the world, and says, "The earth still needs a lot of fixing. I think I'll make a list of things that I'd like to get done on earth." What do you think would appear on that list? What are some of the things that you think God would like to see done on earth right now?

   • How many of the things you listed are able to fit into "The Great Commission" talked about in the study on page 98?

   • How many of them could fit into God's two highest priorities listed in Chapter 11: "Loving God" and "Loving our fellow man" (page 89)?

   • How many of them could fit the three important values of God listed on pages 100-103 (eternal over temporal, spiritual over material, availability over ability)?

2. What are some characteristics of someone who does not have vision for how God could use them to expand His kingdom on earth?

3. What are some characteristics of someone who *does* have vision?

4. What is the "primary imperative" of the Great Commission of Jesus Christ (page 98)?

5. What are some things you can begin doing right now to be part of the fulfilling of the Great Commission?

6. Dawson Trotman, founder of the Navigators wrote a booklet about fulfilling the Great Commission called *Born To Reproduce*. What do you think that title means?

7. Why should we be interested in becoming "spiritual reproducers"? What does this have to do with the fulfilling of the "Great Commission" talked about on page 98?

8. *The Power of Multiplication.* Let's see how we could facilitate a vision for reaching the entire world for Christ through a ministry of disciplemaking. Our strategy will be to disciple another person for one year, concentrating on that person's growth and helping them to get firmly established in their walk with the Lord. Then at the beginning of the second year, the two of us will start discipling two others so that by the end of that year there will be four of us. We will keep doubling our numbers each year in this way. At this rate, how many years will it take us to reach the current world population of six billion people? (Do the math!)

9. What distinguishes a true *mathetes* (disciple) of Jesus Christ from a Christian who only attends church "for what I can get out of it"?

10. Given the definition of "disciple" found on page 99, would you say a brand new Christian could be considered a disciple? What is the main distinguishing characteristic of a disciple?

11. One of the values that God sees as important is the "eternal over the temporal" (page 100). Think of some ways that you could be involved in the three "Eternal Things" you discovered at the bottom of that page.

12. Another value that God sees as important is the "spiritual over the material" (page 101). Most would readily agree that Christians are not supposed to be materialistic – that is, pursuing a lifestyle calculated to accumulate the maximum amount of material goods solely for their own sake. But how far can we carry this? Should we own *nothing?* Always buy the cheapest items whenever we shop? Live in tents and wear one set of clothes until it wears out? Is there a balance we need to consider?

13. If this is a group study, share with the group some of the similarities you observed between yourself and some of "God's Available Heroes" on pages 102 and 103.

14. You made several observations about some of God's important, general plans for you on pages 103 and 104. Which of those plans can you already see God beginning to work in your life?

15. Are you able to single out one of them that makes you the most excited and optimistic about your future?

16. Consider the "Conditional Promises" you studied on page 105. Why do you think God places conditions on the fulfilling of some of His promises? Why doesn't He just lavish us with everything we want?

17. If this is a group study, share with the group some of the Goals you are asking God about as He makes you a man or a woman of vision (page 106). Is there anything your group members or your mentor could do to help you in your pursuit of those Goals?

> "There are no ordinary people. You have never talked to a mere mortal. Nations, cultures, arts, civilization – these are mortal, and their life is to ours as the life of a gnat. But it is immortals whom we joke with, work with, marry, snub and exploit – immortal horrors or everlasting splendors."[2]
> –C. S. Lewis

Additional materials for deeper study:

Available through New Life Resources: 1-800-827-2788:
- *Personal Disciplemaking,* Chapter 20.
- Transferable Concept #7 *How To Help Fulfill The Great Commission.* A booklet that explores vision and commitment from the standpoint of Christians working together world-wide to advance the kingdom of God.

Other books available through your local bookstores or on the web:
- *Born To Reproduce* by Dawson Trotman, founder of The Navigators. This booklet demonstrates that the ultimate purpose for which humans are created is to reproduce spiritually. Available through NavPress.
- *Come Help Change The World* by Bill Bright. The story of how God took Bill and Vonette Bright's vision for reaching the world through college students and forged it into the international ministry of Campus Crusade for Christ. NewLife Publications.
- *Eternal Impact* by Phil Downer of Christian Business Men's Committee. Studies the disciplemaking ministry of Jesus Christ and focuses on how a life-on-life ministry of discipleship can have a profound impact for Christ on the world. Harvest House.
- *Living Above The Level Of Mediocrity* by Charles R. Swindoll. Inspiring book that will help the reader set his or her sights high, strive for excellence, and partner with God's desire to do great things through us.

---

[1] Alcorn, Randy, *In Light Of Eternity* (Colorado Springs, CO: Waterbrook Press, 1999), p. 143.
[2] Lewis, C.S., *The Weight Of Glory* (New York, NY: Macmillan, 1949), pages 18-19; quoted in Randy Alcorn, Ibid., p. 128.

Bonus Chapter
The Devotional Connection . . .
...Your Secret Life With Jesus

Thought/Discussion Questions

Main Objectives of This Study:

That the new Christian would gain the conviction that actively pursuing a loving, living relationship with Jesus Christ is at the core of Christianity, and that he/she would commit to keeping a daily time alone with God, with the motivation being that of deepening his/her relationship with Him.

Thought/Discussion Questions:

1. If you had been Don in the opening scenario, what would you have shared with Debbie to try to change her attitude toward your marriage relationship? What parallels can you draw between this and what many Christians need to hear from Jesus?
2. Read Philippians 3:8 again. What are some of the things that people today must "consider a loss" in order to pursue the highest goal of "knowing Christ Jesus my Lord"?
3. Philippians 4:6 says that we may pray about *everything*. Why do you think some people are reluctant to pray to God about "everything"? [Follow-up question: Do you think God ever finds our prayers tedious, or that He's just too busy with more important things to pay attention to our "petty little requests"?]
4. Most people feel that they don't spend enough time in prayer. Why do you think this is?
5. Which do you think is more important: the quantity or the quality of our prayers?
6. An important ingredient of a healthy prayer life is "Adoration." Write down one thing that you *love* about God. Now write down two more things. This is the essence of Adoration!
7. Another important ingredient mentioned was "Thanksgiving." Write down three things that God's been doing in your life recently for which you are thankful.
8. What does Hebrews 4:12 mean when it says that the Word of God is "living and active"? In what sense is the Bible "alive"?
9. If you're in a group situation, share about a time when you felt that something you read in the Bible had been put there *just for you*.

Illustration for 2 Timothy 3:16-17 to consider or share in a group study: Imagine a picture of a path with footprints on it. The prints go down the center of the path for a while, and then suddenly veer off to the right. They tromp through underbrush, rocks and brambles for a while, and then head to the left, back onto the path. Then they once again continue down the center of the path. These four word pictures illustrate what God's Word provides for us:

Doctrine – To show us the correct path to walk on.

Reproof – To let us know when we've gotten off the path.

Correction – To show us how to get back on the path.

Instruction in Righteousness – To keep us on the path in the future.

10. Read Joshua 1:8 again. The promise at the end of the verse is that those who discuss, meditate on and obey the Word of God would be "prosperous and successful." What do you think this means? Is this a promise that all Christians will become millionaires?

11. Why do you think it would be a good idea to spend a few moments in "heart preparation" as you begin your Quiet Time?

12. Not to say anything against praying while showering, driving to work, waiting in line at the post office, etc., but can you think of some advantages to spending time in concentrated prayer each day with no distractions—such as in your Quiet Time?

13. The study recommended the morning as being the "best" time to have a daily Quiet Time. But what if you're a "night owl," and only semi-conscious until about noon?

14. If you are determined to get up in the mornings and have a Quiet Time, what are some things you can do to ensure that you *will* get up at the designated time?

15. On Sundays, why can't "attending a church service" count as a Daily Devotional time?

16. Men, do you *really* think you can have a Quiet Time while fly fishing?

17. Many people have found "journaling" to be a helpful component in their Quiet Times—that is, writing down things they learn from their Bible study, turning their prayers into "letters" to God, jotting down thoughts that come to their minds throughout the day. Why do you think this might prove to be a positive experience for them? Is it something you'd be interested in trying?

Additional materials for deeper study:

Available through New Life Resources: 1-800-827-2788:
- *Personal Disciplemaking,* pages 262-266.
- *How To Pray—Transferable Concept #9* by Bill Bright (Campus Crusade for Christ). Covers the basics of prayer, including why we pray, to whom we pray, when, and how we can pray with confidence.
- *The Christian and the Bible.* Step #5 in Campus Crusade for Christ's "Ten Basic Steps Toward Christian Maturity." Gives a good overview of the Bible and practical ideas on how to study it.

Other books available through your local bookstores or on the web:
- *Worship: Rediscovering the Missing Jewel* by Ronald Allen and Gordon Borror (Multnomah Press). An inspirational primer on the definition of worship, how to go about it, and it's various aspects. Covers both individual and group worship.
- *Practicing His Presence* by Brother Lawrence (Christian Books). Gives great insights into how we can develop a loving, intimate relationship with Jesus—not only though our Quiet Times, but also in the course of our day-to-day lives.

Would You Like to Know God Personally?

Dear Friend,

Yes, you can know God personally, as presumptuous as that may sound. God is so eager to establish a personal, loving relationship with you that He has already made all the arrangements. He is patiently and lovingly waiting for you to respond to His invitation. You can receive forgiveness of your sin and assurance of eternal life through faith in His only Son, the Lord Jesus Christ.

The major barrier that prevents us from knowing God personally is ignorance of who God is and what He has done for us. Read on and discover for yourself the joyful reality of knowing God personally.

Bill Bright

The following four principles will help you discover how to know God personally and experience the abundant life He promised.

1 God loves you and created you to know Him personally.

God's Love

"God so loved the world, that He gave His only begotten Son, that whoever believes in Him should not perish, but have eternal life."
—**John 3:16** [NAS]

God's Plan

"Now this is eternal life: that they may know You, the only true God, and Jesus Christ, whom You have sent."
—**John 17:3**

What prevents us from knowing God personally?

2 Man is sinful and separated from God, so we cannot know Him personally or experience His love.

Man is Sinful

"All have sinned and fall short of the glory of God."
—**Romans 3:23** [NAS]

Man was created to have fellowship with God; but, because of his own stubborn self-will, he chose to go his own independent way and fellowship with God was broken. This self-will, characterized by an attitude of active rebellion or passive indifference, is an evidence of what the Bible calls sin.

Man is Separated

> "…[Those] who do not know God and do not obey the gospel of our Lord Jesus… will be punished with everlasting destruction and shut out from the presence of the Lord…"
> —**2 Thessalonians 1:8-9** [NAS]

> "The wages of sin is death" [spiritual separation from God]
> —**Romans 6:23a** [NAS]

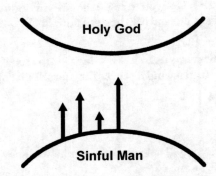

Holy God

Sinful Man

This diagram illustrates that God is holy and man is sinful. A great gulf separates the two. The arrows illustrate that man is continually trying to reach God and establish a personal relationship with Him through his own efforts, such as a good life, philosophy, or religion – but he inevitably fails.

The third principle explains the only way to bridge this gulf…

3 *Jesus Christ is God's only provision for man's sin. Through Him alone we can know God personally and experience God's love.*

He Died in Our Place

> "God demonstrates His own love toward us, in that while we were yet sinners, Christ died for us."
> —**Romans 5:8** [NAS]

He Rose From the Dead

> "Christ died for our sins…He was buried…He was raised on the third day according to the Scriptures… He appeared to Peter, then to the twelve. After that He appeared to more than five hundred…"
> —**1 Corinthians 15:3-6** [NAS]

He is the Only Way to God

> "Jesus said to him, 'I am the way, and the truth, and the life; no one comes to the Father, but through Me.'"
> —**John 14:6** [NAS]

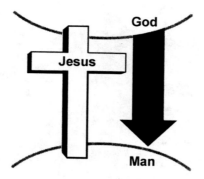

God

Jesus

Man

This diagram illustrates that God has bridged the gulf that separates us from Him by sending His Son, Jesus Christ, to die on the cross in our place to pay the penalty for our sins.

It is not enough just to know these three truths...

 We must individually receive Jesus Christ as Savior and Lord; then we can know God personally and experience His love.

We Must Receive Christ

"As many as received Him, to them He gave the right to become children of God, even to those who believe in His name."

—**John 1:12** [NAS]

We Receive Christ Through Faith

"By grace you have been saved through faith; and that not of yourselves, it is the gift of God; not as a result of works, that no one should boast."

—**Ephesians 2:8-9** [NAS]

When We Receive Christ, We Experience A New Birth

Read
John 3:1-8
in your Bible.

We Receive Christ by Personal Invitation

[Christ speaking] "Behold, I stand at the door and knock; if any one hears My voice and opens the door, I will come in to him."

—**Revelation 3:20** [NAS]

Receiving Christ involves turning to God from self (repentance) and trusting Christ to come into our lives to forgive us of our sins and to make us what He wants us to be. Just to agree intellectually that Jesus Christ is the Son of God and that He died on the cross for our sins is not enough. Nor is it enough to have an emotional experience. We receive Jesus Christ by faith, as an act of our will.

These two circles represent two kinds of lives:

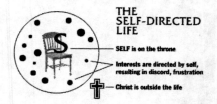

THE
SELF-DIRECTED
LIFE

SELF is on the throne

Interests are directed by self, resulting in discord, frustration

Christ is outside the life

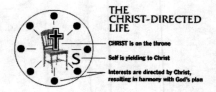

THE
CHRIST-DIRECTED
LIFE

CHRIST is on the throne

Self is yielding to Christ

Interests are directed by Christ, resulting in harmony with God's plan

Which circle best represents your life?

Which circle would you like to have represent your life?

The following explains how you can receive Christ:

You Can Receive Christ Right Now by Faith Through Prayer

(Prayer is talking with God)

God knows your heart and is not so concerned with your words as He is with the attitude of your heart. The following is a suggested prayer:

> **"Lord Jesus, I want to know You personally. Thank you for dying on the cross for my sins. I open the door of my life and receive You as my Savior and Lord. Thank You for forgiving me of my sins and giving me eternal life. Take control of the throne of my life. Make me the kind of person You want me to be."**

Does this prayer express the desire of your heart?

If it does, pray this prayer right now, and Christ will come into your life, as He promised.

How to Know That Christ Is in Your Life

Did you receive Christ into your life? According to His promise in Revelation 3:20, where is Christ right now in relation to you? Christ said that He would come into your life and be your friend so that you can know Him personally. Would He mislead you? On what authority do you know that God has answered your prayer? (The trustworthiness of God Himself and His Word.)

The Bible Promises Eternal Life to All Who Receive Christ

> "The witness is this, that God has given us eternal life, and this life is in His Son. He who has the Son has the life; he who does not have the Son of God does not have the life. These things I have written to you who believe in the name of the Son of God, in order that you may know that you have eternal life."
> —1 John 5:11-13 [NAS]

Thank God often that Christ is in your life and that He will never leave you (Hebrews 13:5). You can know on the basis of His promise that Christ lives in you and that you have eternal life from the very moment you invite Him into your life. He will not deceive you.

An important reminder...

Do Not Depend on Feelings

The promise of God's Word, the Bible – not our feelings – is our authority. The Christian lives by faith (trust) in the trustworthiness of God Himself and His Word. This train diagram illustrates the relationship among **fact** (God and His Word), **faith** (our trust in God and His Word), and **feeling** (the result of our faith and obedience) (John 14:21).

The train will run with or without the caboose. However, it would be useless to attempt to pull the train by the caboose. In the same way, we as Christians do not depend on feelings or emotions, but we place our faith (trust) in the trustworthiness of God and the promises of His Word.

Now That You Have Entered Into a Personal Relationship With Christ...

The moment you received Christ by faith, as an act of your will, many things happened, including the following:

1. Christ came into your life (Revelation 3:20 and Colossians 1:27).
2. Your sins were forgiven (Colossians 1:14).
3. You became a child of God (John 1:12).
4. You received eternal life (John 5:24).
5. You began the great adventure for which God created you (John 10:10; 2 Corinthians 5:17 and 1 Thessalonians 5:18).

Can you think of anything more wonderful that could happen to you than entering into a personal relationship with Jesus Christ? Would you like to thank God in prayer right now for what He has done for you? By thanking God, you demonstrate your faith.

To enjoy your new relationship with God...

Suggestions for Christian Growth

Spiritual growth results from trusting Jesus Christ. A life of faith will enable you to trust God increasingly with every detail of your life, and to practice the following:

> "The righteous man shall live by faith."
> —**Galatians 3:11**
> [NAS]

G – Go to God in prayer daily (John 15:7).

R – Read God's Word daily (Acts 17:11). Begin with the Gospel of John.

O – Obey God moment by moment (John 14:21).

W – Witness for Christ by your life and words (Matthew 4:19; John 15:8).

T – Trust God for every detail of your life (1 Peter 5:7).

H – Holy Spirit – Allow Him to control and empower your daily life and witness (Galatians 5:16-17; Acts 1:8).

Fellowship In a Good Church

God's Word admonishes us not to forsake "the assembling of ourselves together..." (Hebrews 10:25). Several logs burn brightly together; but put one aside on the cold hearth and the fire goes out. So it is with your relationship with other Christians. If you do not belong to church, do not wait to be invited. Take the initiative; call the pastor of a nearby church where Christ is honored and His Word is preached. Start this week, and make plans to attend regularly.[1]

---

[1] This publication "Would You Like To Know God Personally?" is available in booklet form from NewLife Publications (800) 827-2788. This is a version of the Four Spiritual Laws, written by Bill Bright. Copyright 1965, 1988, Campus Crusade for Christ, Inc.

Principles for Memorizing Scripture

The following principles are taken from The Navigators' "Topical Memory System," available from NavPress (call 1-800-366-7788 or visit their web site: www.navpress.com.)[1]

As you start to memorize a verse—

1. Read in your Bible the context of each verse you memorize.

2. Try to gain a clear understanding of what each verse actually means. (You may want to read the verse in other Bible translations or paraphrases to get a better grasp of the meaning.)

3. Read the verse through several times thoughtfully, aloud or in a whisper. This will help you grasp the verse as a whole. Each time you read it, say the topic, reference, verse, and then the reference again.

4. Discuss the verse with God in prayer, and continue to seek His help for success in memorizing Scripture.

While you are memorizing the verse—

5. Work on saying the verse aloud as much as possible.

6. Learn the topic and reference first.

7. After learning the topic and reference, learn the first phrase of the verse. Once you have learned the topic, reference, and first phrase and have repeated them several times, continue adding more phrases after you can quote correctly what you have already learned.

8. Think about how the verse applies to you and your daily circumstances.

9. Always include topic and reference as part of the verse as you learn and review it.

After you can quote correctly the topic, reference, verse and reference again—

10. It is helpful to write the verse out. This deepens the impression in your mind.

11. Review the verse immediately after learning it, and repeat it frequently in the next few days. This is crucial for getting the verse firmly fixed in mind, because of how quickly we tend to forget something recently learned.

12. REVIEW! REVIEW! REVIEW! Repetition is the best way to engrave the verses on your memory. (Studies show that daily reviewing memorized Scripture for thirty days causes it to become firmly incorporated into your heart and mind.)

---

[1]*Topical Memory System* (Colorado Springs, CO: NavPress, 1969, 1981), pp. 13-14. Used by permission.

The Topical Memory System is an excellent tool for getting established in the discipline of Scripture memory. By the time you've completed their Scripture memory course, you will have successfully (and solidly) learned sixty key verses arranged in five series:
- Series A — "Live the New Life"
- Series B — "Proclaim Christ"
- Series C — "Rely on God's Resources"
- Series D — "Be Christ's Disciple"
- Series E — "Grow in Christlikeness"

Two Wells Illustration

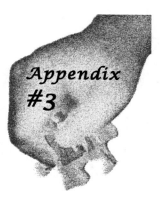

This is a graphic representation of "The Parable of the Two Wells" covered in Chapter 4 – *The Victory Connection.* It's also included in this study's companion book *Personal Disciplemaking* (Chapter 12). It's included here so that you can see the flow of the parable, but also to give you an illustration that you could incorporate into your own ministry opportunities. You can explain the "Victory" concepts contained in Chapter 4 in a very memorable fashion by simply drawing this illustration on a blank sheet of paper. In this way, you can help a younger Christian understand the tension that exists within between his "Old Nature" and his "New Nature," and how he can take steps to lessen the influence of the Old and increase the influence of the New.

As you read through the parable in Chapter 4, the corresponding graphic actually starts on the right side of the picture, with the "farmer" (your mind) between his farm house and his well. The story then moves to the left side of the page where the farmer drills a new well into a new, pure aquifer (corresponding to salvation). The hill in the center of the graphic represents the difficulties and temptations that keep a Christian from drawing from the new well (his New Nature) and deciding to draw from his old well instead. The scripture at the bottom-middle of the illustration highlight the keys to victory.

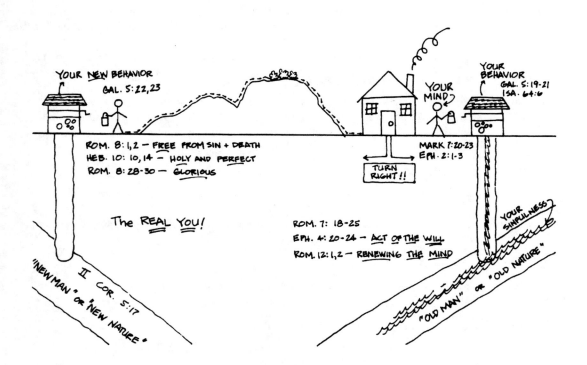

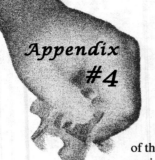

Spiritual Warfare Ammunition Bunker

Use these scriptures when involved in spiritual warfare (Chapter 10). They are your "sword of the Spirit, which is the word of God" (Ephesians 6:17). Remember how Jesus used this weapon against Satan when He was tempted in the wilderness (Matthew 4:1-11): "It is written…"

Anger

Proverbs 16:32 – He who is slow to anger is better than the mighty, and he who rules his spirit, than he who captures a city.

James 1:20 – For man's anger does not bring about the righteous life that God desires.

Deceit/Lying

Leviticus 19:11-12 – Do not steal. Do not lie. Do not deceive one another. Do not swear falsely by My name and so profane the name of your God. I am the Lord.

Proverbs 12:22 – The Lord detests lying lips, but He delights in men who are truthful.

Disobedience to God

John 14:21 – Whoever has My commands and obeys them, he is the one who loves Me; and he who loves Me will be loved by My Father, and I too will love him and show Myself to him.

1 Samuel 15:22b – To obey is better than sacrifice, and to heed is better than the fat of rams.

Disrespect for Authority

Ephesians 5:21 – Submit to one another out of reverence for Christ.

1 Peter 2:13-14 – Submit yourselves for the Lord's sake to every authority instituted among men; whether to the king, as the supreme authority, or to governors, who are sent by Him to punish those who do wrong and to commend those who do right.

Drugs & Alcohol

Proverbs 20:1 – Wine is a mocker and beer a brawler; whoever is led astray by them is not wise.

Ephesians 5:18 – Do not get drunk on wine, which leads to debauchery. Instead, be filled with the Spirit.

Envy

Galatians 5:26 – Let us not become conceited, provoking and envying each other.

Proverbs 14:30 – A heart at peace gives life to the body, but envy rots the bones.

Fearfulness

Isaiah 41:10 – Do not fear, for I am with you; do not be dismayed, for I am your God. I will strengthen you and help you; I will uphold you with My righteous right hand.

2 Timothy 1:7 – For God did not give us a spirit of timidity, but a spirit of power, of love and of self-discipline.

Greed/Coveting

Exodus 20:17 – You shall not covet...

Matthew 16:26 – What good will it be for a man if he gains the whole world, yet forfeits his soul?

Hatred

Leviticus 19:17 – Do not hate your brother in your heart...

1 John 4:20 – If anyone says, "I love God," yet hates his brother, he is a liar. For anyone who does not love his brother, whom he has seen, cannot love God, whom he has not seen.

Idolatry

Exodus 20:4 – You shall not make for yourself an idol in the form of anything in heaven above or on the earth beneath or in the waters below.

1 John 5:21 – Dear children, keep yourselves from idols.

Jealousy

Proverbs 27:4 – Anger is cruel and fury overwhelming, but who can stand before jealousy?

Romans 13:13 – Let us behave decently, as in the daytime...not in dissension and jealousy.

Lack of Faith

Romans 1:17 – ...the righteous will live by faith.

Hebrews 11:6 – And without faith it is impossible to please God, because anyone who comes to Him must believe that He exists and that He rewards those who earnestly seek Him.

Laziness

Proverbs 6:9-11 – How long will you lie there, you sluggard? When will you get up from your sleep? A little sleep, a little slumber, a little folding of the hands to rest - and poverty will come on you like a bandit and scarcity like an armed man.

Colossians 3:23 – Whatever you do, work at it with all your heart, as working for the Lord, not for men.

Lust

2 Timothy 2:22 – Flee the evil desires of youth, and pursue righteousness, faith, love and peace, along with those who call on the Lord out of a pure heart.

1 Peter 2:11 – Dear friends, I urge you, as aliens and strangers in the world, to abstain from sinful desires, which war against your soul.

Malice

1 Peter 2:1 – Therefore, rid yourselves of all malice and all deceit...

1 Peter 2:16 – ...not using your liberty for a cloak of maliciousness, but as the servants of God.

Materialism

Hebrews 13:5 - Keep your lives free from the love of money and be content with what you have, because God has said, "Never will I leave you; never will I forsake you."

Luke 12:15 - Then He said to them, "Watch out! Be on your guard against all kinds of greed; a man's life does not consist in the abundance of his possessions."

Pride

1 Peter 5:5-6 – ...Clothe yourselves with humility toward one another, because, "God opposes the proud but gives grace to the humble." Humble yourselves, therefore, under God's mighty hand, that He may lift you up in due time.

Proverbs 29:23 – A man's pride brings him low, but a man of lowly spirit gains honor.

Profanity

Ephesians 4:29 – Do not let any unwholesome talk come out of your mouths, but only what is helpful for building others up according to their needs, that it may benefit those who listen.

Ephesians 5:3-4 – But among you there must not be even a hint of ... obscenity, foolish talk or coarse joking, which are out of place, but rather thanksgiving.

Rebellion

Proverbs 17:11 – An evil man is bent only on rebellion…

Romans 13:2 – He who rebels against the authority is rebelling against what God has instituted, and those who do so will bring judgment on themselves.

Revenge

Leviticus 19:18 – Do not seek revenge or bear a grudge against one of your people, but love your neighbor as yourself. I am the Lord.

Proverbs 25:21–22 - If your enemy is hungry, give him food to eat; if he is thirsty, give him water to drink. In doing this, you will heap burning coals on his head, and the Lord will reward you.

Matthew 6:14–15 - For if you forgive men when they sin against you, your heavenly Father will also forgive you. But if you do not forgive men their sins, your Father will not forgive your sins.

Self-centered

Proverbs 12:15 – The way of a fool seems right to him, but a wise man listens to advice.

Philippians 2:3-4 – Do nothing out of selfish ambition or vain conceit, but in humility consider others better than yourselves. Each of you should look not only to your own interests, but also to the interests of others.

Slander/Gossiping

Proverbs 10:18 - He who conceals his hatred has lying lips, and whoever spreads slander is a fool.

Ephesians 4:29 - Do not let any unwholesome talk come out of your mouths, but only what is helpful for building others up according to their needs, that it may benefit those who listen.

Sullenness

Psalm 118:24 – This is the day the Lord has made; let us rejoice and be glad in it!

Philippians 4:4 – Rejoice in the Lord always. I will say it again: Rejoice!

Theft

Exodus 20:15 – You shall not steal.

1 Peter 4:15 – If you suffer, it should not be as a murderer or thief or any other kind of criminal...

Unforgiving Spirit

Matthew 18:21-22 – "...Lord, how many times shall I forgive my brother?" ...Jesus answered, "I tell you, not seven times, but seventy times seven."

Matthew 6:14-15 – For if you forgive men when they sin against you, your heavenly Father will also forgive you. But if you do not forgive men their sins, your Father will not forgive your sins.

Wrath/Rage

Psalm 37:8 – Refrain from anger and turn from wrath; do not fret – it leads only to evil.

Proverbs 12:16 – A fool's wrath is quickly and openly known, but a prudent man ignores an insult.

Reproducible Forms

Following this page are several items, which you have permission to copy as often as needed.

Wow!/Verse/Do/Huh? Bible Study Method

This form can be copied and put in a Bible Study notebook. Or you can just use it as a guide to make your own. This method of Bible Study is described in chapter 7, *The Bible Connection*, on page 57, and also referenced on page 129.

Read the Bible in a Year

This form (two pages) can be copied back-to-back, folded and inserted in your Bible for easy reference and tracking. This schedule of reading will help you read through the Bible in a year, six days/week. You can start at any point and either put the date you read the passage on the completion line, or you can just check it off. Put the year on the top to track the years through which you make this your practice. This reading schedule is referenced on pages 57 and 129.

Prayer Diary

These two forms give you an idea of how you can keep your prayer diary. The half-page diary form can be copied back-to-back, folded and inserted into your Bible for easy reference as you pray. The full-page diary form would be useful in a larger prayer notebook. You can copy these pages or design your own. The Diary is described in chapter 8, *The Prayer Connection*, on page 67.

Bible Study: Book_____ Chapter_____

Wow! (The thing that *amazes* me the most in this chapter.)

Verse (The *verse* I liked most in this chapter — write it out.)

Do (Something I need to *do* in response to reading this chapter.)

Huh? (*Questions* that came to my mind as I read this chapter.)

Read the Bible in a Year

You can start this reading plan at any time, beginning with any book of the Bible. There is a portion of Scripture to read each weekday and each weekend. Mark in the *Completed* column the date you read the passage. Copy this plan and put it in your Bible for quick reference. **Helpful Hint:** To make it through this program within a year, plan to *just read!* Going deeper and *studying* each day's assignment would be valuable, but it could slow your pace to the point of discouragement.

Day	Passage	Completed
Weekend	**Genesis 1-3**	
Monday	Genesis 4-9	
Tuesday	Genesis 10-12	
Wednesday	Genesis 13-16	
Thursday	Genesis 17-20	
Friday	Genesis 21-24	
Weekend	**Genesis 25-28**	
Monday	Genesis 29-32	
Tuesday	Genesis 33-36	
Wednesday	Genesis 37-40	
Thursday	Genesis 41-43	
Friday	Genesis 44-47	
Weekend	**Genesis 48-50**	
Monday	Exodus 1-3	
Tuesday	Exodus 4-6	
Wednesday	Exodus 7-9	
Thursday	Exodus 10-12	
Friday	Exodus 13-15	
Weekend	**Exodus 16-18**	
Monday	Exodus 19-21	
Tuesday	Exodus 21-24	
Wednesday	Exodus 25-27	
Thursday	Exodus 28-31	
Friday	Exodus 32-35	
Weekend	**Exodus 36-38**	
Monday	Exodus 39-40	
Tuesday	Leviticus 1-3	
Wednesday	Leviticus 4-7	
Thursday	Leviticus 8-11	
Friday	Leviticus 12-15	
Weekend	**Leviticus 16-20**	
Monday	Leviticus 21-23	
Tuesday	Leviticus 24-27	
Wednesday	Numbers 1-4	
Thursday	Numbers 5-8	
Friday	Numbers 9-12	
Weekend	**Numbers 13-16**	
Monday	Numbers 17-20	
Tuesday	Numbers 21-25	
Wednesday	Numbers 26-30	
Thursday	Numbers 31-33	
Friday	Numbers 34-36	
Weekend	**Deut. 1-4**	
Monday	Deut. 5-7	
Tuesday	Deut. 8-11	
Wednesday	Deut. 12-16	
Thursday	Deut. 17-20	
Friday	Deut. 21-25	
Weekend	**Deut. 26-29**	
Monday	Deut. 30-32	
Tuesday	Deut. 33-34	
Wednesday	Joshua 1-5	
Thursday	Joshua 6-8	
Friday	Joshua 9-12	
Weekend	**Joshua 13-17**	
Monday	Joshua 18-21	
Tuesday	Joshua 22-24	
Wednesday	Judges 1-5	
Thursday	Judges 6-8	
Friday	Judges 9-12	
Weekend	**Judges 13-16**	
Monday	Judges 17-21	
Tuesday	Ruth	
Wednesday	1Samuel 1-3	
Thursday	1Samuel 4-8	
Friday	1Samuel 9-12	
Weekend	**1Samuel 13-15**	
Monday	1Samuel 16-19	
Tuesday	1Samuel 20-23	
Wednesday	1Samuel 24-26	
Thursday	1Samuel 27-31	
Friday	2Samuel 1-4	
Weekend	**2Samuel 5-7**	
Monday	2Samuel 8-10	
Tuesday	2Samuel 11-14	
Wednesday	2Samuel 15-18	
Thursday	2Samuel 19-20	
Friday	2Samuel 21-24	
Weekend	**1Kings 1-4**	
Monday	1Kings 5-8	
Tuesday	1Kings 9-11	
Wednesday	1Kings 12-16	
Thursday	1Kings 17-19	
Friday	1Kings 20-22	
Weekend	**2Kings 1-3**	
Monday	2Kings 4-8	
Tuesday	2Kings 9-12	
Wednesday	2Kings 13-17	
Thursday	2Kings 18-21	
Friday	2Kings 22-25	
Weekend	**1Chron 1-7**	
Monday	1Chron 8-12	
Tuesday	1Chron 13-18	
Wednesday	1Chron 19-25	
Thursday	1Chron 26-29	
Friday	2Chron 1-5	
Weekend	**2Chron 6-8**	
Monday	2Chron 9-12	
Tuesday	2Chron 13-16	
Wednesday	2Chron 17-20	
Thursday	2Chron 21-25	
Friday	2Chron 26-28	
Weekend	**2Chron 29-32**	
Monday	2Chron 33-36	
Tuesday	Ezra 1-3	
Wednesday	Ezra 4-6	
Thursday	Ezra 7-8	
Friday	Ezra 9-10	
Weekend	**Nehemiah 1-2**	
Monday	Nehemiah 3-4	
Tuesday	Nehemiah 5-7	
Wednesday	Nehemiah 8-10	
Thursday	Nehemiah 11-13	
Friday	Esther 1-2	
Weekend	**Esther 3-4**	
Monday	Esther 5-7	
Tuesday	Esther 8-10	
Wednesday	Job 1-3	
Thursday	Job 4-7	
Friday	Job 8-10	
Weekend	**Job 11-14**	
Monday	Job 15-17	
Tuesday	Job 18-19	
Wednesday	Job 20-21	
Thursday	Job 22-24	
Friday	Job 25-28	
Weekend	**Job 29-31**	
Monday	Job 32-34	
Tuesday	Job 35-37	
Wednesday	Job 38-39	
Thursday	Job 40-42	
Friday	Psalm 1-6	
Weekend	**Psalm 7-12**	
Monday	Psalm 13-18	
Tuesday	Psalm 19-24	
Wednesday	Psalm 25-30	
Thursday	Psalm 31-36	
Friday	Psalm 37-41	
Weekend	**Psalm 42-47**	
Monday	Psalm 48-53	
Tuesday	Psalm 54-59	
Wednesday	Psalm 60-66	
Thursday	Psalm 67-72	
Friday	Psalm 73-77	
Weekend	**Psalm 78-82**	
Monday	Psalm 83-89	
Tuesday	Psalm 90-97	
Wednesday	Psalm 98-103	
Thursday	Psalm 104-106	
Friday	Psalm 107-111	

Day	Reading	Completed
Weekend	Psalm 112-118	
Monday	Psalm 119	
Tuesday	Psalm 120-127	
Wednesday	Psalm 128-135	
Thursday	Psalm 136-139	
Friday	Psalm 140-144	
Weekend	Psalm 145-150	
Monday	Proverbs 1-4	
Tuesday	Proverbs 5-9	
Wednesday	Proverbs 10-13	
Thursday	Proverbs 14-17	
Friday	Proverbs 18-21	
Weekend	Proverbs 22-24	
Monday	Proverbs 25-29	
Tuesday	Proverbs 30-31	
Wednesday	Ecclesiastes 1-6	
Thursday	Ecclesiastes 7-12	
Friday	S. Solomon 1-4	
Weekend	S. Solomon 5-8	
Monday	Isaiah 1-3	
Tuesday	Isaiah 4-7	
Wednesday	Isaiah 8-12	
Thursday	Isaiah 13-20	
Friday	Isaiah 21-27	
Weekend	Isaiah 28-30	
Monday	Isaiah 31-35	
Tuesday	Isaiah 36-39	
Wednesday	Isaiah 40-42	
Thursday	Isaiah 43-45	
Friday	Isaiah 46-48	
Weekend	Isaiah 49-52	
Monday	Isaiah 53-57	
Tuesday	Isaiah 58-62	
Wednesday	Isaiah 63-66	
Thursday	Jeremiah 1-6	
Friday	Jeremiah 7-10	
Weekend	Jeremiah 11-15	
Monday	Jeremiah 16-20	
Tuesday	Jeremiah 21-25	
Wednesday	Jeremiah 26-29	
Thursday	Jeremiah 30-33	

Day	Reading	Completed
Friday	Jeremiah 34-36	
Weekend	Jeremiah 37-39	
Monday	Jeremiah 40-45	
Tuesday	Jeremiah 46-52	
Wednesday	Lamentations	
Thursday	Ezekiel 1-6	
Friday	Ezekiel 7-11	
Weekend	Ezekiel 12-15	
Monday	Ezekiel 16-19	
Tuesday	Ezekiel 20-24	
Wednesday	Ezekiel 25-28	
Thursday	Ezekiel 29-32	
Friday	Ezekiel 33-36	
Weekend	Ezekiel 37-39	
Monday	Ezekiel 40-43	
Tuesday	Ezekiel 44-48	
Wednesday	Daniel 1-3	
Thursday	Daniel 4-6	
Friday	Daniel 7-9	
Weekend	Daniel 10-12	
Monday	Hosea 1-3	
Tuesday	Hosea 4-6	
Wednesday	Hosea 7-8	
Thursday	Hosea 9-11	
Friday	Hosea 12-14	
Weekend	Joel	
Monday	Amos 1-2	
Tuesday	Amos 3-5	
Wednesday	Amos 6-7	
Thursday	Amos 8-9	
Friday	Obadiah	
Weekend	Jonah	
Monday	Micah 1-2	
Tuesday	Micah 3-5	
Wednesday	Micah 6-7	
Thursday	Nahum	
Friday	Habakkuk	
Weekend	Zephaniah	
Monday	Haggai	
Tuesday	Zechariah 1-2	
Wednesday	Zechariah 3-6	

Day	Reading	Completed
Thursday	Zechariah 7-8	
Friday	Zechariah 9-11	
Weekend	Zechariah 12-14	
Monday	Malachi 1-2	
Tuesday	Malachi 3-4	
Wednesday	Matthew 1-4	
Thursday	Matthew 5-7	
Friday	Matthew 8-10	
Weekend	Matthew 11-13	
Monday	Matthew 14-18	
Tuesday	Matthew 19-23	
Wednesday	Matthew 24-25	
Thursday	Matthew 26-28	
Friday	Mark 1-3	
Weekend	Mark 4-7	
Monday	Mark 8-10	
Tuesday	Mark 11-13	
Wednesday	Mark 14-16	
Thursday	Luke 1-2	
Friday	Luke 3-6	
Weekend	Luke 7-9	
Monday	Luke 10-12	
Tuesday	Luke 13-15	
Wednesday	Luke 16-18	
Thursday	Luke 19-21	
Friday	Luke 22-24	
Weekend	John 1-3	
Monday	John 4-6	
Tuesday	John 7-9	
Wednesday	John 10-12	
Thursday	John 13-17	
Friday	John 18-21	
Weekend	Acts 1-2	
Monday	Acts 3-7	
Tuesday	Acts 8-9	
Wednesday	Acts 10-12	
Thursday	Acts 13-14	
Friday	Acts 15-18	
Weekend	Acts 19-20	
Monday	Acts 21-23	
Tuesday	Acts 24-26	

Day	Reading	Completed
Wednesday	Acts 27-28	
Thursday	Romans 1-3	
Friday	Romans 4-5	
Weekend	Romans 6-8	
Monday	Romans 9-11	
Tuesday	Romans 12-16	
Wednesday	1Cor 1-6	
Thursday	1Cor 7-10	
Friday	1Cor 11-14	
Weekend	1Cor 15-16	
Monday	2Cor 1-5	
Tuesday	2Cor 6-9	
Wednesday	2Cor 10-13	
Thursday	Galatians	
Friday	Ephesians	
Weekend	Philippians	
Monday	Colossians	
Tuesday	1Thessalonians	
Wednesday	2Thessalonians	
Thursday	1Timothy	
Friday	2Timothy	
Weekend	Titus, Philemon	
Monday	Hebrews 1-3	
Tuesday	Hebrews 4-6	
Wednesday	Hebrews 7-9	
Thursday	Hebrews 10-11	
Friday	Hebrews 12-13	
Weekend	James	
Monday	1Peter	
Tuesday	2Peter	
Wednesday	1John	
Thursday	2John	
Friday	3John, Jude	
Weekend	Revelation 1-3	
Monday	Revelation 4-6	
Tuesday	Revelation 7-9	
Wednesday	Revelation 10-14	
Thursday	Revelation 15-18	
Friday	Revelation 19-20	
Weekend	Revelation 21-24	

Prayer Diary

Date	Request	Answer

Prayer Diary

Date	Request	Answer

Prayer Diary

Date	Request	Answer

 **DISCIPLE-MAKERS** To order the following materials, copy and mail or fax *both* sides of this form to us.
INTERNATIONAL

Payment options:

   If you prefer to pay for the materials with a check, please call our office for shipping charges and sales tax. If you pay with a credit card we will add the shipping and sales tax to your order. We accept Master Card, Visa and Discover Card. We charge for actual shipping costs plus $.50 handling fee. Sales tax applies to the "Shipping Address." International orders must be paid via credit card.

Shipping options:

   We normally ship Priority Mail through the US Postal Service. If you need faster service, prefer a different carrier, or are willing to wait for the less expensive, "slow boat" service, please indicate your requirements.

Discount options:

   We offer volume discounts on the items marked by §, and discounts to Campus Crusade for Christ staff on all materials. Please contact us for more information.

Item	Price	Quantity	Total
Connecting With God § A companion tool for *Personal Disciplemaking*, this Bible study series addresses foundational connection points with God. Includes twelve chapters (plus a bonus chapter), Thought/Discussion Questions for group study, and Assessment questions to determine which chapters should be studied. ISBN 0-9671227-3-2	$15.99	_____	$ _____
Personal Disciplemaking § This book, by Chris Adsit, presents a long-term, disciple-sensitive, training objective-oriented approach to one-on-one and small group disciplemaking. 384 pages. Re-published by Integrated Resources, Orlando FL, 1998. ISBN 1-57902-022-4	$13.99	_____	$ _____
Personal Disciplemaking Tool Kit § This supplemental material to the book, *Personal Disciplemaking*, contains eight Self-Assessment Questionnaires, Key and Instructions, Disciple's Growth Profile Chart and the poster-sized Disciplemaking Growth Grid.	$6.00	_____	$ _____
Spanish Personal Disciplemaking Tool Kit	$6.00	_____	$ _____
"Mini" Personal Disciplemaking Kit The "Mini" Kit contains just the "Christian Fundamentals" material from the full Tool Kit. It can be used as a "quick assessment" tool. Because it is less intimidating than the full Kit, it has proven effective in training Christians in the process of making disciples. (Also available in Adobe Acrobat format on our web site.)	$.50	_____	$ _____
Spanish "Mini" Kit	$.50	_____	$ _____
Polish "Mini" Kit	$.50	_____	$ _____
Personal Disciplemaking Video Training Series Western Seminary in Portland, Oregon, teamed up with Disciplemakers International to produce this video series designed to train Christians to become disciplemakers. The series, taught by Chris Adsit, has 24 thirty-minute sessions on eight VHS tapes, and is designed to work in a class setting or in a small group. Skits help to visually demonstrate the lessons. The accompanying Leader's Guide contains discussion questions and reproducible student notes for each session. ISBN 0-9671227-0-8	$125.00	_____	$ _____
Personal Disciplemaking Video Training Series, PAL Format	$94.95	_____	$ _____
Disciplemaker's Encyclopedia Resource materials for the disciplemaker to use when addressing specific topics. Contains Bible studies and articles which can be reproduced for use with the disciple. Also contains overview, Biblical basis for the topic, great quotes, illustrations, other resources, troubleshooting helps, and evaluation ideas. [A work-in-process: only two "Resource Packages" are available at this printing.]			
RP001 Assurance of Salvation	$5.50	_____	$ _____
RP110c Praying With Others	$4.50	_____	$ _____

Total: $ _____

Disciplemakers International
PO Box 2212
Eugene, OR 97402
U.S.A
Voice: 541-345-3458
Toll-free within the USA: 1-888-342-2235
Fax: 541-345-4249
email: disciplemaker@compuserve.com
Internet: www.ccci.org/disciplemakers

Billing Address:

Name _____

Company _____

Address _____

City _____

State/Province _____

Zip/Postal Code _____

Country _____

Contact Phone _____

Credit Card: _____-_____-_____-_____

Expiration Date _____/_____

Signature: _____

Campus Crusade Staff Account for account transfers

Account # _____

If your organization is tax-exempt, Tax-exempt ID:

ID # _____

Shipping Address (if different from Billing Address):

Name _____

Company _____

Address _____

City _____

State/Province _____

Zip/Postal Code _____

Country _____

Contact Phone _____

Special Shipping Instructions: _____

_____

_____